The
Edict of Nantes

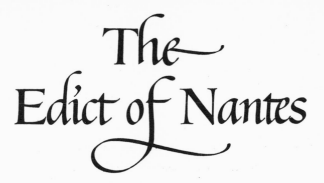

The Edict of Nantes

by

Noel B. Gerson

Illustrated by Bob Pepper

GROSSET & DUNLAP
PUBLISHERS / NEW YORK

Contents

The
Edict of Nantes

1

The Upside-Down Decree

Few documents in human history have had a greater long-range effect upon mankind than the Edict of Nantes. It was the first written promise to grant specific religious freedoms to a persecuted minority.

Promulgated, or issued as a royal decree, in 1598 by King Henry IV of France, it has left its stamp upon civilization hundreds of years later. The twentieth-century ecumenical movement inaugurated by Pope John XXIII is a direct outgrowth of the Edict of Nantes. If Catholics and Protestants are growing closer, if there is a greater spirit of brotherhood uniting Christians and Jews, the Edict of Nantes is partly responsible.

Amazing contradictions surround the Edict of Nantes; from the outset, it was an "upside-down" document.

The Edict was revised and changed, edited and rewritten so many times during the first five years after it was published that no one, including scholars who have spent their entire lives studying it, knows for certain which version was the original. Unlike the American Declaration of Independence or the Eng-

lish Magna Carta, it was not a clear-cut statement of high principles. It was long and detailed, laboriously spelling out the pre-
cise rights that the King of Catholic France, himself a Protestant
twice converted to Catholicism, was granting his Protestant subjects.

In some versions the Edict of Nantes runs to seventy or eighty
large parchment pages, closely written. Moreover, in almost
every version and on almost every page, there are scribbled dele-
tions and additions. It is a wonder that any one, including Henry
himself, ever knew exactly what rights were being granted.

Yet, even though violent conflicts were required to settle every
detail, the details were far less important than the fact that the
decree was issued in the first place. It brought to an end the
bloody religious conflicts that had split France for decades, and
it paved the way toward true religious tolerance by men of all
faiths.

It is a near miracle that the Edict of Nantes was written and
finally issued. Two men in particular were responsible for its
preparation, and they spent five years at the task. One was a
Catholic, President Jean Jeannin of the Parliament of Normandy, the highest-ranking provincial justice in the realm. The
other was a Protestant and Henry's Chancellor, Philippe de
Montauban.

The Edict appeared harmful to Jeannin's best interests, yet he
fought hard for its passage. After it was promulgated, he demanded strict obedience to it in letter as well as spirit. Montauban, on the other hand, worked reluctantly on it, even though
its provisions served him well. It was his duty as chief law officer
of the kingdom to ensure that it was obeyed, but for five years

he looked the other way when its provisions were broken and at times actively connived against it.

Meanwhile the Catholic cardinals and bishops of France, who had been bitterly opposed to its promulgation, advocated strict obedience to it.

The Edict also had upside-down effects outside the borders of France. Queen Elizabeth I of England liked to think of herself as the Protestant champion of Europe. But the Edict dismayed her, and she sent a special messenger to King Henry for the purpose of registering her vehement protest. The decree had the opposite effect on the strongest of Catholic monarchs, King Philip II of Spain. Philip was a dour man who rarely smiled and was known to be notably lacking in a sense of humor. But the report circulated through Europe that when he heard the Edict had been issued, he laughed until tears of joy came to his eyes.

Perhaps the greatest contradiction occurred almost a century after the Edict was promulgated. In 1685 Henry's grandson, King Louis XIV, the most autocratic of rulers, revoked the Edict of Nantes. This act revived religious bigotry and was the signal for the renewal of the persecution of Protestants in France. But Louis, unwittingly, accomplished more for universal religious tolerance than his grandfather had done.

Some of the contradictions are easy to explain. President Jeannin favored the Edict and wanted it obeyed because he was afraid the Protestants would be granted even more rights. Chancellor de Montauban saw an opportunity to obtain more for his fellow Protestants, and so he was lax in enforcing the provisions of the decree.

Queen Elizabeth of England was afraid that Henry was granting too many *political*—not religious—concessions to his nobles. These rights made them stronger at the expense of the crown. Elizabeth, like Henry, ruled her subjects with an iron hand and wanted nothing to weaken the basic power of a fellow monarch.

Philip of Spain was in an unhappy situation, having suffered two major defeats in a decade. His Armada, a great fleet of warships, had been beaten and scattered when attempting to invade England in 1588. In addition, Spain had been the principal supporter of the Catholic cause in France. But Henry, who had won and kept his crown, had achieved a series of victories over Philip's proud legions. Now, still humiliated, Philip made another mistake in judgment. An ignorant, superstitious man, he literally believed that by granting religious freedom to Protestants, Henry was opening the door of France to the devil. Satan, Philip believed, would achieve what he himself had not been able to accomplish and would destroy his archfoe, Henry.

The attitude of the French cardinals and bishops grew out of more complicated causes. For more than one hundred years the highest-ranking officials of the Roman Catholic Church in France had been increasingly dependent on the crown. They paid only lip service to the pope, and in most matters took their orders from the king. Indeed, they owed their very appointments to the monarchy. Only in questions of a strictly theological nature were they able to assert their independence.

They viewed the Edict of Nantes as a weakening of the firm tie that bound church and state in France. The more rigorously the decree was obeyed, in their opinion, the more the bond would be loosened. It was their hope that, like the bishops of the Middle Ages who had preceded them, they would become the real masters of France.

Perhaps the greatest of the Edict of Nantes' contradictions was that most nobles, Protestant and Catholic alike, regarded the decree as a document relating to secular rather than religious affairs. Freedom of conscience was of relatively minor importance to them. Like the bishops, they were concerned with the struggle for power between the crown and the nobles. Many of the country's leading families had been losing prestige and influence. They saw the Edict as a weapon they could use to fight their way back to power. But the minor nobles, whose stature had increased during the long, dreary civil wars, saw the decree as a threat to their standing. Consequently they opposed it.

The growing middle class, which could be found only in the larger cities, viewed the Edict of Nantes exclusively in economic terms. For more than one hundred years the monarchy had been pampering the wealthy merchants, ship owners and manufacturers. These men, in turn, had been sharing their increasing profits with the royal family. Under the complicated terms of the Edict of Nantes, privileges were granted to a new class. And that class, the merchants feared, would compete with them for royal favors.

It is a paradox that only the poor appreciated the ultimate significance of the Edict of Nantes. For generations the lives of peasants and artisans had been disrupted. Some Catholic, some Protestant, all were devout in their religious beliefs. When the civil wars had started, they had needed no urging to volunteer for military duty in the opposing armies.

But decades of betrayal had made them as cynical as they were weary. Nine separate religious wars had been fought in less than a half century. The poor had seen their leaders make agreements and sign treaties, and then ruthlessly fail to keep their promises. Great nobles on both sides had issued calls to arms in the name of God, but had fought only for their own advancement.

The slaughter had been endless. Every poor family mourned the loss of a husband, a son or a brother. Men who had been maimed or injured in battle could be found in every town, village and rural district. The poor were heartily sick of the conflict and yearned for permanent peace.

They, of all Frenchmen, sincerely believed in the principles of religious tolerance. They wanted to live and let live; they were willing to respect a neighbor's faith, provided their own was respected in return.

King Henry IV understood and shared this burning desire of the poor. He also knew why the nobles and higher clergy felt as they did, and he sympathized with Elizabeth of England. Only for Philip of Spain did he feel abiding contempt.

In its truest sense, the Edict of Nantes was Henry's creation. The very idea of granting freedom of religion originated with him. He guided the men who framed the document, repeatedly forcing them to enlarge its scope. Only a monarch of his courage, wisdom and cunning could have issued the decree—and enforced it.

He recognized the Edict as a religious document granting

personal freedom to thousands of his subjects. He knew it was a political document as well, and he realized far better than did his nobles and bishops what effect it would have on their power. He was sensitive to it as an economic force in the lives of the middle class. And, being farsighted, he knew it would influence the colonization of the New World, one of his most ambitious projects.

Henry was a genius—a great statesman, soldier, planner, builder and administrator. In order to understand what the Edict of Nantes contained and why, it is necessary to understand the dramatic life of the man known to posterity as Henry the Great.

2

The Making of a King

THE man who led France out of the Middle Ages into the modern world was the ruthless, efficient King Louis XI, who reigned from 1461 to 1483. He built a strong royal army, suppressed rebellious and ambitious nobles, and, governing without a parliament or congress, taxed his subjects as he saw fit.

More important than all else, he strengthened the crown at the expense of the Roman Catholic Church. For centuries the bishops had ruled their dioceses like little kingdoms. Louis XI brought them to heel.

His work made it relatively easy for a later successor, the energetic Francis I, to force an agreement on Pope Leo X. Beginning in 1516 when the Concordat of Bologna was signed, the French crown guaranteed the annual payment of contributions by the faithful to the Vatican. The Pope, however, lost his power to appoint bishops in France. That right was assumed by the crown.

Francis also continued Louis' work of strengthening the monarchy at the expense of the nobility. Great families that had held princely powers for centuries fumed and squirmed, but Francis attacked one at a time, making it difficult for them to band together against them.

It was during the reign of Francis, which ended in 1547, that the great wave of opposition to the Church (known as the Reformation) first struck France. For almost one hundred and fifty years it had become increasingly obvious to thinking men that the Church was in need of reform. All-powerful for centuries, she had become corrupt and lazy. Men everywhere suffered from her abuses.

But a series of councils failed to right the wrongs, although the time was ripe for change. In 1517 an obscure German monk, Martin Luther, defied the authority of the Church, and the Reformation was under way.

A French priest and lawyer, Jean Chauvin, who was a generation younger than Luther, brought the Reformation to France. Calling himself by the Latin name John Calvin, he established his own sternly moral sect in Geneva, Switzerland. His followers, who were known as Huguenots, crossed the border into France, and there his ideas spread swiftly.

Two classes in particular were susceptible to Calvin's Protestantism: the very wealthy aristocrats and the sorely oppressed poor. Both were motivated, at least in part, by a deep-rooted sense of rebellion. The great nobles found their power curtailed more and more by the crown with each passing generation. They also found that the monarchy had gained control of the Church in France. The new religion quite literally gave them the opportunity to *protest*. Many nobles became Huguenots as a way of expressing their opposition to the crown.

The poor were driven to Protestantism by desperation. The lot of French peasants and artisans had never been easy, but until 1516 the people had been adept at playing the crown and the Church against each other. Thereafter it became impossible to employ such tactics. The monarchy conscripted its subjects into its armies and taxed the people at will. The Church, crown-controlled, added another burden of taxation. And, when Calvin appeared, the poor flocked to his Huguenot banner because they had nowhere else to turn.

Francis I made the tactical error of trying to suppress the Huguenots. A poet of the time notes that whenever a man was arrested as a heretic, two others became Huguenots; whenever a Huguenot was put to death for his faith, four others joined the Protestant movement.

King Henry II continued the policies of Francis and tried to smash the Huguenots. At last the nobles had a cause, and all who resented the increasing authority of the crown banded together under the flag of John Calvin's faith. Although the Huguenots always were a minority, they became a very powerful minority.

Some historians estimate that by 1562, when the first of the religious civil wars broke out in France, approximately fifty percent of the important, land-owning French nobles were Huguenots. According to the most conservative estimate, at least one third of the wealthy nobles had become Protestants.

Far more significant than these statistics was the nature of those who became Protestants. Certainly they were the most alert, intelligent and aggressive members of the nobility, those who most resented being overwhelmed by the monarchy. Certainly, as events proved, a high percentage of the most talented and courageous soldiers became Huguenots.

Henry II died in an accident in 1559. Although he had been a man of some force, he left behind a weak and obnoxious brood. His widow, Catherine de Médicis, an ambitious, scheming Italian princess, wanted to rule France herself. This she did through her three sons, all of whom were weaklings. Francis II, who died in 1560, knew nothing about the duties of a king and cared less. Charles IX, who died in 1574, was a pawn in the hands of his mother Henry III, the best of the brothers, who died in 1589, was an amiable bumbler susceptible to the influence of the last person who spoke to him.

Henry II and Catherine also had a daughter, Margaret of Valois, who was destined to play a major role in making the history that led to the promulgation of the Edict of Nantes. Margaret was the loveliest woman of her day, and poets in many lands celebrated her beauty. She also proved to be the most treacherous and dissolute woman of the age. It was the misfortune of Henry the Great that she became his first wife, for because of her he almost lost his life.

When the inept sons of Henry II came to the throne one after the other, the Protestant nobles saw their chances to recoup their lost power. Led by such great warriors as the Prince de Condé, the Duc de Montmorency and Admiral Gaspard de Coligny, they applied constant pressure on the monarchy, demanding the restoration of their ancient rights and privileges.

Another element was added to the explosive situation by the wily, ambitious de Guise family, prominent Catholic aristocrats who ruled the semi-independent duchy of Lorraine. Through one brother, the Duc de Guise, and another, the Cardinal of Lorraine, the family hoped to seize the throne from Catherine de Médicis and her sons. This could best be done, they reasoned, by building a powerful army and waging a "holy war" on the Huguenots. Obviously, they had to be rid of the powerful nobles if they hoped to gain—and keep—control of the country. The de Guise family wanted not only to stamp out heresy, but even more, to rule all France.

Queen Mother Catherine, on behalf of herself and her sons, was forced to move warily. The Huguenot nobles, she knew, were not seeking the throne; their demands were relatively more modest. They merely wanted to expand their own restricted power. Therefore the ambitious de Guise family was the greater menace.

Unfortunately, her position was weakened by the popularity of the de Guise cause. Their rallying cry was that of stamping out heresy, while she could only offer the mild alternative of asking for loyalty to the crown. She bided her time, and at last the opportunity to win broad Catholic support arrived when her daughter, Margaret, was married to young King Henry of Navarre, who was later to become Henry IV.

There was nothing in the background of this young man to indicate that he would grow into the greatest leader France had known in her long history. When Henry was born in the little town of Pau in the Pyrenees on December 14, 1553, the event was considered minor outside the immediate family circle.

His father, Antoine de Bourbon, was Duc de Vendôme, a nobleman of high social standing, but without power. He was descended from Louis IX, the monarch who had been canonized twenty-seven years after his death, and so Antoine and Henry could claim a king of France as their ancestor. They were considered minor nobles, however, because they were descended from St. Louis' sixth son, Robert of Clermont. Many others took precedence in the line of succession to the throne of France.

There was more cause for rejoicing on the other side of the family. Henry's mother was Jeanne d'Albret, Queen of Navarre, a tiny kingdom tucked in the Pyrenees Mountains between France and Spain. Its traditions and language were French, but its strongly independent people had accepted the teachings of John Calvin with great enthusiasm. Virtually the whole kingdom, nobles and commoners alike, had become Protestant, and so it was assumed that Henry would be brought up in the reformed faith. His father, although nominally a Catholic, agreed with the plan.

Henry became the monarch of his own realm at birth under a regency headed by his parents. Antoine was a selfish man who pursued his own pleasures, and he had little influence on his son. But Queen Jeanne was enormously ambitious for Henry. Later in his life he paid her tribute, saying that she was responsible for all he accomplished.

When the boy was four years old his parents took him to the court of Henry II at Amiens. There the small, dark-haired child created little stir. Although he was a member of royalty, he was just a distant cousin of Henry II's three sons. In 1561 young Henry was sent to the College of Navarre, in Paris, where he spent four years.

Then, in 1565, he began his higher education at a Protestant

seminary in Bern, Switzerland. As a result of his three years
there he was known in his own day as "the Bernaise." His grades
were excellent, and he showed the first signs of the driving
ambition he was to demonstrate all of his life. When he wrote
a theme or report, he was never satisfied with a paper that was
less than perfect.

Henry's formal education ended in 1568, when the so-called
"Third War of Religion" broke out in France. The fifteen-
year-old boy was taken out of school by his mother and sent
off to join the Protestant army commanded by hard-bitten
Admiral de Coligny. The following year, when Henry was
sixteen, he astonished his elders by distinguishing himself in
the Battle of Arnay-le-Duc in the province of Burgundy. The
senior officers of his cavalry regiment were killed in action, and
so Henry took command. He led his troops in one furious
charge after another and drove the Catholic forces of the de
Guise family from the field.

His courage was taken for granted, but he displayed qualities
of leadership that were extraordinary. In fact, he showed the
instinctive grasp of both the tactics of battle and the strategy
of military campaigns that was to make him the most renowned
general of his era. A close friend and companion, Henry de
Montmorency, who later inherited his own father's duchy and
became the military deputy of Henry IV, was a wise young
man. Watching the young King of Navarre in battle, he wrote
to his family, "Our King is going to become a very great man."

Henry did not return to school, but remained in the field for
almost four years. There he learned the life of a soldier. There
he learned to study human nature, too. And it is significant

that he continued to read constantly, spending most of his evenings hunched over a book in his tent.

The year 1572 was the most significant in young Henry's life. His mother died early in the year, and he became the monarch of Navarre in fact as well as name. He had also moved much closer to the throne of France. The wars of religion had taken a heavy toll of royalty, and only two men now stood between him and the crown. One was King Charles IX, and the other was the King's younger brother, who was to become Henry III.

Catherine de Médicis decided to take no chances. She did not like the idea of accepting a Protestant "heretic" into her immediate family, but she thought it wise to have Henry of Navarre nearby where she could keep watch on him. There was a truce that had halted the fighting in the war, and so the Queen Mother proposed that Henry marry her daughter, Margaret.

Henry accepted. Perhaps he was dazzled by Margaret's celebrated beauty. Certainly he was quick to grasp the chance to move closer to the French throne. The wedding was held in the main chapel of the Louvre, the royal palace in Paris. It was large enough to accommodate the many invited guests, but not the general public. Under ordinary circumstances the people of Paris would have been free to attend the ceremony, but the Catholic Church could not publicly approve of the marriage of Princess Margaret, sister of King Charles of France, to a "heretic." And so the wedding was not held in the great cathedral, Notre Dame.

By this time Henry of Navarre had become the symbol,

although not yet the leader, of the Huguenots. Dozens of prominent Protestant noblemen accepted the invitation to his wedding. The presence of so many hated foes under one roof gave Queen Catherine and her advisers an idea as wicked as it was cruel.

They could, the Queen Mother decided, destroy two enemies with a single blow. Bands of hired murderers could kill off all the Huguenot leaders. This would render the ordinary Protestants helpless, and their movement would collapse. At the same time, this assault would prove to the Catholics of France that King Charles IX and Queen Mother Catherine were the true protectors of their faith, and the influence of the de Guise family would be weakened, perhaps permanently.

A series of balls, receptions and other social celebrations was planned over a two-week period before and after the wedding of Margaret and Henry of Navarre. Queen Mother Catherine decided to have all the Huguenot leaders killed at the same time by hired assassins during the festivities. Then the plans were broadened: all Huguenots in Paris, including the common people, would be put to death at once. Several regiments of troops loyal to Queen Catherine were assigned the task, and their officers were sworn to secrecy.

Margaret, working with her mother, took an active part in the conspiracy. The bride was assigned the task of persuading her husband of less than a week to join her in her sitting room at the Louvre. Had Margaret succeeded, her husband's life would have been ended by the killer's knives. The history of France thereafter would have been far different, and the history of religious tolerance would have been significantly altered.

As it was, the events that led directly to the Edict of Nantes more than a quarter of a century later resulted from an accident. On the morning of August 23, 1572, the tragedy known as the St. Bartholomew's Day Massacre, which raged for two days began. On this morning, Henry of Navarre quarreled with his bride, and after leaving the palace went for a walk with his Huguenot friend, the noted author of the period, Agrippa d'Aubigné.

The assassins who rushed into Margaret's suite did not find Henry. The monarch of Navarre, who was to strike a great blow for religious freedom in 1598, was safe—for the moment.

Meanwhile the Massacre gathered speed throughout Paris. The city's poor Catholics, who knew no better, joined Queen Catherine's troops in a search for Huguenots. Protestants were slaughtered everywhere, from the Louvre to their own modest homes. A crowd caught Admiral de Coligny outside his house and knifed him in cold blood.

Hundreds of nobles managed to escape, at least temporarily. Most of those who went into hiding, however, were found, dragged into the open, and killed. In all, thousands of Huguenots were killed in Paris on August 23d and 24th, while hundreds perished in the smaller cities of France.

Henry of Navarre owed his life to his own remarkable presence of mind. He and Agrippe d'Aubigné were strolling near Notre Dame when the rioting started and he heard the shout, "Death to all Huguenots!" Knowing he would be recognized and murdered, he reacted instantly.

Dragging his startled friend with him, Henry hurried into the cathedral. There he stripped off his cape of gold cloth with

its fur collar, his silver spurs, his rings and other signs of wealth. Clad only in his black doublet, breeches and boots, he looked like a poor student. Wisely he resisted the temptation to appear in public armed and got rid of his sword, too. Then he snatched a prayer book from a young priest. Holding it against his chest where it could be seen by the mobs, he walked slowly back to the Louvre, still accompanied by his friend. The crowds, thinking him a pious Catholic, did not molest him, and he reached the Louvre unharmed.

Too late Henry realized that he had jumped from the frying pan into the fire. Margaret gave an alarm, and he was seized by royal troops. But he did not lose his wits and again saved his life by rapid thinking. He had decided to give up the Huguenot faith, he announced, and was ready to become a Catholic. The troops refused to molest him, and Queen Catherine's own confessor received him into Catholicism.

King Charles was relieved, and the treacherous Margaret said she was pleased. Henry's sudden conversion did not fool Queen Catherine, however, but she kept her thoughts to herself.

Henry did the same, making no comment when the Queen Mother said, "The Huguenot cause in France is dead!" He had his own ideas on the subject.

A wave of horror spread through the Protestant nations of Europe when news of the Massacre became known. But the Catholics, particularly Philip II of Spain, publicly rejoiced. Even Pope Gregory XIII, an enlightened man who did much to reform the Church from within, made the mistake of allowing zealous partisans to strike a medal bearing his name in honor of the Massacre.

Religious hatreds throughout all of Europe were intensified, and the opposing camps prepared for a final, conclusive battle. That battle was long delayed because Henry of Navarre, who overnight became the symbol of Protestantism in France, was a prisoner in the palace of his mother-in-law. Armed guards were assigned to Henry supposedly to protect him, but actually, as he discovered when he tested them by riding to the north gate of the city, to prevent him from leaving Paris.

The St. Bartholomew's Day Massacre was a temporary victory for a bigoted, cruel woman, but a great man emerged from the tragedy. Henry of Navarre formed new ambitions and goals. His cool reasoning was a miracle of intellectual self-discipline. He knew that France would not survive as a nation if the religious wars lasted indefinitely. If the nation hoped to survive, Catholics and Protestants would have to work together.

He realized that the Catholic majority would not surrender power voluntarily. Therefore the Huguenots would have to force them to make concessions. The only force men understood was that of combat, and so he planned to lead a mighty Protestant host into the field. Eventually men of good will on both sides would want a peaceful compromise, and with their help he would force both Catholics and Protestants to make peace.

Since a king of Navarre could not force Frenchmen to do his bidding, Henry could achieve his will only by taking the throne of France. This, he thought, would not be too difficult. King Charles was in poor health. His younger brother, the future Henry III, who had helped his mother plan the Massacre, was a weakling; it would be easy to dispose of him at the appropriate time. For the moment, however, Henry kept his plans to himself. It was enough that he knew his own mind.

For many months Catherine kept him a prisoner at the Louvre, where he was barely on speaking terms with his wife due to her prominent role in his attempted murder. Then, in 1573 Charles IX died, and Henry III, completely dominated by his mother, ascended the throne. Henry of Navarre, brooding in his Louvre apartment, spent most of his time reading political, military and economic treatises. Each day, when he was alone, he exercised to keep fit.

It was during this period that he conceived of the document that became the Edict of Nantes. According to the diaries of Agrippe d'Aubigné, who remained at the palace with him, he dreamed of forcing Frenchmen of all religious persuasions to accept universal tolerance. For a long time, however, the dream remained impractical.

Other Huguenots managed, one by one, to escape from closely guarded Paris. Even d'Aubigné finally managed to break free, and he carried the good word to Protestant nobles that their leader was anxiously awaiting the opportunity to join them. Young Henry de Montmorency and Charles, Duc de Biron, another Huguenot leader, quietly continued to recruit their forces in the provinces.

At sundown on February 2, 1576, Henry of Navarre managed to elude his guards and to ride unchallenged through the gates of Paris. At last he was free, and raced south to join his supporters.

A lesser man would have been vindictive, but Henry insisted that he wanted fair play, not revenge. Everywhere, to his surprise, huge crowds greeted him, and everywhere he repeated his message: he sought religious freedom for men of all faiths. All—Catholics, Protestants and Jews—would be equal under his banner.

Naturally, Protestants and Jews enlisted in his service. To the dismay of Catherine de Médicis and Henry III and to the horror of the de Guise family, large numbers of Catholic leaders also joined him. These men, sick of Catherine's cruelty and despising the de Guise greed, wanted a peaceful, prosperous and united France. Henry of Navarre offered them their only hope of such a future.

Only a man of Henry's stature could have persuaded the Huguenot nobles to accept such a goal. They yearned not only to avenge the blood bath of St. Bartholomew's Day, but also, it must be rembered, to increase their own power.

Henry privately had no intention of sharing power with them when he became monarch of France. But on this subject, like so many others, he kept his own counsel. "Do you want to practice your faith openly, anywhere in France?" he demanded. "If you do, follow me!"

The Huguenots, some in spite of misgivings, followed him. So great was his hold on the Catholics who accepted him that they did not desert him when he announced that he had become a Catholic in order to save his life, and was reverting to the Protestant faith.

The stage was set for one of history's most remarkable dramas.

3

Paving the Way
to a Great Document

I<small>N</small> 1576 Henry of Navarre formed a mighty army. In it he accepted all men of good faith, Huguenots and Catholics alike, men who were willing to accept those of other faiths as their equals. And for the first time in the history of France, Jews were encouraged to enlist under his banner, too. A man's faith, Henry declared, was his own business. He was responsible only to God for his religious beliefs.

The concept was unique. Henry was not motivated solely by a deep love of religious freedom, to be sure. His primary concern was temporal, not spiritual. He wanted to unite France, to end her civil wars, and to put all of her people to work building the nation. His goals were glory and prosperity, not tolerance alone. In order to achieve his ends he needed religious freedom, and in struggling toward them he gave the world its first taste of religious liberty.

The bigots, both Catholic and Protestant, were shocked and dismayed. The de Guise family formed a temporary alliance with Queen Mother Catherine and an organization called the

Catholic League. Its purpose was simple: help would be obtained from outside sources to destroy the upstart from Navarre. Philip of Spain was the first to respond to the League's appeal, and he sent troops as well as money to the de Guise family. Thus the war in France took on an international character.

The Huguenots, whose attitude toward their religious foes was as unyielding as that of League members, found themselves in an uncomfortable position. If they rejected the stand taken by Henry of Navarre, they had nowhere else to turn. For better or worse they had to accept his extraordinary notion that men of all faiths could and should live together as brothers.

The Protestant monarchs of Europe were displeased by Henry's ideas, too. But like the bigoted Protestants, they were caught in a trap. If they refused to help Henry, the Catholic bigots would triumph. When Philip of Spain committed himself to the cause of the League, Elizabeth of England lost her alternatives. No matter how much she might condemn Henry in private, she had to help him or see her nation's greatest foe gain a strong foothold in France. And so England sent money and troops to Henry.

The bulk of the new army, however, was made up of moderates. Huguenots, Catholics and Jews who were weary of civil war saw the opportunity to end the fighting and create a stable France. Nobles and commoners, city dwellers and men who lived in the country streamed into Henry's camp.

Now Henry of Navarre displayed true military genius. He struck so swiftly that his enemies could not organize against him. There was no battle; instead, his enemies fled when he approached. The de Guise family managed to withdraw their

legions in an orderly manner and to retreat to their citadel of
Lorraine. But the regiments of Queen Mother Catherine and
young Henry III were scattered. Their army literally melted
away.

Henry of Navarre held the upper hand and made the most
of it. First, he forced Catherine to accept humiliating conditions in an agreement that came to be known as the Treaty of
Beaulieu. She was compelled to appoint Henry of Navarre
Lieutenant General, or the King's deputy, of the huge southern
province of Guienne. This area adjoined his own little kingdom,
Navarre, and for all practical purposes he added it to his own
realm, ruling it as though he already sat on the throne of
France.

Now he had a strong base of operations, and he continued
to recruit men for his army. In 1577, using the threat of renewed
warfare, he compelled Henry III to sign the Treaty of Bergerac,
which revoked the worst of the laws that discriminated against
Huguenots. Men who admitted they were Protestants could
no longer be put to death by burning at the stake. The property
of Huguenots could no longer be confiscated and given to the
Roman Catholic Church. The children of Huguenots could no
longer be forced against their will to become Catholics.

Henry of Navarre had made a beginning, but it was a shaky
start. On paper it appeared that an improvement had been made,
but in practice the results were negligible. The Queen Mother
and her weakling son made no attempts to enforce the provisions of the Treaty of Bergerac. When Henry protested, which
he did frequently, Catherine replied by inviting him to confer
in Paris.

He had no intention of being captured and held as a prisoner again, and so he refused. Instead he traveled elsewhere in France, persuading moderates of all faiths to join him. For three years he had no permanent home and made his way through France recruiting and pleading for his cause. His main base was located in the city of Bordeaux, and when he returned there for a brief visit in 1579 he found Margaret waiting for him. She had been sent by her mother to persuade him to adopt a less militant stand and to try to convince him that he should disband his regiments.

Henry, of course, had no intention of listening to his treacherous wife. In fact, he showed his contempt by seizing the revenues from Margaret's extensive estates and used the money to help pay the costs of his still-growing army. Then, to the astonishment of those who realized he was making an open, final break with the ruling family, he sent the daughter of Queen Catherine to a remote castle he owned in the Auvergne Mountains near the little village of Usson.

There the lovely Margaret spent the next twenty years her husband's prisoner. She was free to lead her own life, but was forbidden to travel more than twenty miles from the castle. Her fate caught the imagination of many authors, and countless romances were written about her. Henry, however, knew her true nature and assigned hard-headed guards to make certain that his orders were obeyed.

Catherine de Médicis, who actually cared little about her daughter, used Margaret's banishment as an excuse to declare the Treaty of Bergerac null and void. This was an invitation to the Catholics of France to renew their persecution of Huguenots, and Henry could not tolerate such a situation.

And so, in 1580, he renewed his war against the crown. Leading his army in a whirlwind campaign that took him from one end of France to the other, he won a series of triumphs. By the end of 1580 the forces of the de Guise family had suffered a major defeat, and the regiments of Catherine had been crushed. Henry of Navarre forced Henry III to sign still another treaty, and the crown promised to halt the persecution of Huguenots.

For another three and a half years there was an uneasy truce. Henry of Navarre kept his army in the field, even though the cost of maintaining his regiments strained his slender resources. Although he was considered the great Protestant champion of Europe by this time, he was so poor that he owned only two suits of clothes. But as he often told Henry de Montmorency, he needed only his armor.

Catherine and her son were wealthy, thanks to the revenues that poured into the royal treasury, but the new Duc de Guise, whose name was also Henry, was even richer. Not a penny of the revenues from Lorraine went into the crown treasury, and all of the funds from abroad contributed to the Catholic League were kept by the de Guise family.

By 1584 Queen Catherine and Henry de Guise both felt the time had come to put down the upstart from Navarre. Gold had rebuilt the crown armies, the League had been strengthened by recruits from Spain and the Italian states, and the League's generals, who were in overall command, felt that Henry of Navarre could be beaten at last.

Henry III was persuaded by his mother to issue the formal challenge. This the King did by issuing a proclamation that specifically excluded Henry of Navarre from the right to succeed to the throne. Although first in line, he no longer could call himself the Dauphin, or crown prince.

He replied with expected vigor, and the flimsy peace was shattered by what is known as the War of the Three Henrys. The League foolishly allowed its forces to be lured into Henry of Navarre's stronghold, Guienne. Although larger, better equipped and better armed, the League army suffered a series of devastating defeats during the next two years. This created problems almost impossible to solve.

Queen Catherine and her son, who had been depending upon the de Guise family to save them, suspected that they were being betrayed. Aware that their own forces were inadequate to beat Henry of Navarre, they opened negotiations with him. Duc Henry de Guise protested vehemently.

Catherine solved the problem by arranging the murder of the duke and his brother. The new head of the House of Guise was Charles, Duc de Mayenne, the most competent member of the clan. A man who enjoyed food so much that he weighed more than three hundred pounds, he was an able field commander, a first-rate administrator, and a ruthless human being. He retaliated by driving the Queen Mother and Henry III out of Paris.

Deprived of her capital, Catherine was forced to ask her son-in-law, Henry of Navarre, for his support. He gave it to her, but at a high price. Henry III was compelled to recognize him, a distant cousin, as the official heir to the throne, and he was also obliged to promise an end to the persecution of Huguenots.

Henry of Navarre knew the pledge was virtually useless, but his immediate aim was the creation of a legal precedent for what he hoped to do when he came into power in his own right. He reached the throne sooner than he had anticipated. In January, 1589, Queen Mother Catherine died, and the Protestant champion was left as the real ruler of the country. The frightened, ineffectual Henry III signed every document presented to him by his cousin.

Then, on August 1, 1589, a madman assassinated the "cardboard" king, and the monarch of Navarre ascended the throne of France, taking the title of Henry IV.

The Catholic League immediately intensified its activities against him. Philip of Spain sent twenty-five thousand of his best troops from Belgium, which at that time was a Spanish possession. Catholic princes in the southern German and the Italian states sent another twenty-five thousand. Money poured into the League's coffers from every Catholic ruler of Europe. It appeared that a world war, in miniature, would be fought on religious grounds in France.

Before the reinforcements could arrive, however, the inspired Henry IV defeated Mayenne in a vicious battle fought at the little town of Arques, in northern France. That was the beginning of the final phase of the struggle.

More and more Frenchmen, regardless of their religious beliefs, rallied to the banner of the legitimate monarch, Henry IV. More and more Spanish troops were sent to Mayenne, and when he said they were too few for him to operate effectively, others were dispatched from the Papal States of Italy. Henry won major victory after major victory, and suffered only minor reverses.

His own army was composed of Frenchmen; Huguenots, Catholics and Jews fought side by side. Their opponents, under Mayenne, were foreigners. The overwhelming majority were Spanish; the rest, either Italian or German. Many French nobles who had been reluctant to take Henry's part now joined him. Their patriotism was greater than their religious prejudices.

By the late spring of 1593 Henry IV held virtually all of France except Paris. The capital nominally remained in the hands of the League, but actually Henry's resistance came from a far different source. The Huguenots had been either murdered or driven out by the St. Bartholomew's Day Massacre twenty-one years earlier. Only Catholics lived in Paris, and they listened to the advice of their bishops, who were opposed to the presence on the throne of a relapsed "heretic."

Henry had two choices. The first was as difficult as it was cruel: he could place Paris under siege and starve it into submission. But the idea did not appeal to him or to his principal advisers, Biron, Montmorency and Montauban. Perhaps the most incisive thinker in the immediate circle around the King was Maximilien de Béthune, soon to be made Duc de Sully by his master.

A brilliant financier and administrator who would play a major role in making Henry a great monarch, Sully saw the situation clearly. There was little doubt, he said, that an attack on Paris would succeed, although it would take a long time.

But a siege would do more harm than good. Much of the capital would be destroyed by Henry's artillery. Thousands of Parisians would be killed and wounded. And the survivors would become their ruler's bitter, lifelong enemies. Sully advised that an attack on Paris should be avoided at all costs.

The alternative was breathtaking. The Catholic bishops of Paris and its surrounding network of small towns, four in all, had just made Henry a secret offer. If he would become converted to Catholicism again and remain a Catholic, the gates of Paris would be opened to him and the people would welcome him.

Without exception King Henry's close advisers were Huguenots, and most of them were horrified by the proposal. Montmorency, the most valiant soldier in the realm, declared he would rather die storming the walls of Paris. Biron echoed his sentiment. Montauban, a lawyer, said the Catholic Church was trying to achieve through trickery what it had not been able to accomplish by force.

Only Sully urged the King to weigh the offer with care before making up his mind. Henry was quick to grasp his point. The observance of forms meant less to him, by far, than the attainment of his ultimate goal: the complete unification of France.

The King pondered the question for weeks, then summoned his council members into secret session. It was at this meeting that he supposedly made the most cynical statement ever uttered by a great leader.

"Paris," Henry allegedly said, "is well worth a Mass."

4

The Stage Is Set for Tolerance

D ID Henry IV really say, "Paris is well worth a Mass"? Historians have been debating the question for centuries. A very few have clung to the belief that his conversion to Catholicism was sincere. The vast majority, however, agree that Henry resorted to an expediency. They are convinced that he went through the motions of accepting Catholicism in order to unite France.

The facts appear to bear out this opinion. Henry's Huguenot advisers accepted his decision with remarkable calm. Surely the fiery Montmorency, who hated Catholics, would have abandoned the King and retired to his own estates in the south of France had he believed the conversion honest. But he remained at Henry's side for years, and so did all of the others, including the sons and brothers of men who had been murdered on St. Bartholomew's Day.

The records are scant. It appears that no nobleman wanted to put his private thoughts on paper. Mails were uncertain, and trouble might have developed for the duke or baron who even hinted that the King was only pretending.

The many Catholic nobles who had joined Henry were equally calm. They held no celebrations, and they, too, wrote no letters. It must be remembered that most of the lords surrounding Henry were moderates, men who placed the peace and unity of France above *any* religious considerations.

What was more, the nobles who lived at the turn of the seventeenth century were realists. For decades France had been weakened by religious civil wars. The personal fortunes of the lords had declined, and many had been forced to sell portions of their estates in order to meet their expenses. They had every reason for wanting precisely what Henry wanted. And so if they knew or suspected that his conversion was a deception, it served their own advantage not to mention what they saw or heard.

Henry launched into a series of discussions with a number of Catholic bishops who were his supporters, among them Cardinal de Bourbon of Paris, his own cousin. Only one point bothered him. Did the Pope have authority over the King?

The Cardinal's reply was blunt: "He has absolute authority in all matters spiritual, and in regard to temporal matters, can interfere, to the prejudice of kings and kingdoms."

The reply did not satisfy Henry, who was determined to be the sole master of his own realm. What would happen, he wanted to know, if he and the Pope should disagree on a temporal matter concerning the welfare of the people of France?

According to the written accounts of several eyewitnesses attending the meeting, among them both laymen and priests,

Cardinal de Bourbon laughed as he replied. He could not imagine the possibility, he said, that such a situation would arise.

The Archbishop of Bourges agreed. So did the Bishops of Chartres, Nantes, Le Mans and Pérrone, and the Bishop-elect of Evreux.

Henry was content. It seems to have been implicitly understood by everyone present that only one man, Henry of Navarre, would sit on the throne of France.

News of the meeting soon reached Paris, and huge crowds gathered in the streets to cheer. The officers of the League, who were holding a meeting in the city, became alarmed. A special appeal, called an exhortation, was issued to all French Catholics and was signed by three cardinals and eight bishops. The document stated that Henry's forthcoming conversion was not valid. It added that any Catholic who accepted it as valid would be excommunicated from the Church.

Henry ignored the exhortation, and so did the Catholics of Paris. The conversion ceremony was scheduled to take place on July 25, 1593, at the Church of St. Denis, in a small town in the hills overlooking Paris. Thousands of citizens walked from the capital to see the historic event.

Henry and Cardinal de Bourbon had agreed it would be unwise for the King's cousin to officiate at the ceremony. The Vatican would be sensitive, and the League had already registered its opposition. Nothing would be gained by rubbing salt in open wounds. And so the Archbishop of Bourges was in charge, assisted by the others who had taken part in the conference.

The crowds cheered for hours after the conversion. That night Henry rode to another village on a hill, Montmartre, and bonfires were lighted. The flames could be seen in Paris, below, and it became plain that Henry was waging deliberate psychological warfare against the League.

Mayenne, the Spaniards and the Catholic prelates opposed to Henry had only one weapon left: the Pope. If he refused to accept Henry's conversion, they could continue their struggle against him. But Henry, as usual, stole a march on his foes. He sent a party of ambassadors to Rome, and his envoys were the first to arrive there. Pope Gregory may have had doubts regarding the sincerity of the King's conversion, but he certainly was willing to accept the act at face value. The Church, as he saw it, had everything to gain.

Late in February, 1594, Henry received word that the Pope had agreed to accept him into the Church. The cardinals and bishops who had opposed him no longer had any legal or ecclesiastical basis for their objections. Mayenne, realizing that his own hands were tied, quietly sent word to Henry that, at an appropriate time, he would swear his allegiance to the King.

In March, 1594, Henry IV rode in triumph through the streets of Paris to his palace, the Louvre, the same building in which he had spent so many months as the prisoner of Queen Mother Catherine. An era had ended, and a new epoch had begun.

In all, the reign of Henry IV was a remarkable time, and the King demonstrated amazing energy and breadth of vision. Corrupt and incompetent officeholders were replaced by able men loyal to the crown. The nation's debts were wiped out, and

Sully amassed a huge treasury reserve. Henry encouraged foreign trade, gave generous aid to the farmers, and introduced several industries which have been important in France down to the present day. Among them were tapestry weaving and the manufacture of silk, wool and glassware.

A network of canals made it easier to transport goods inside the country. Merchants were able to expand their enterprises because they could obtain loans from the bankers at the lowest rates of interest ever paid up to that time. A new navy was built, and the army was completely reorganized. Henry was interested in the arts, too, and added new wings to the major palaces of Paris, the Louvre and the Tuileries.

It was he who recognized the enormous potential of French discoveries in the New World. He spent huge sums of money financing expeditions to explore further on the North American continent. While he sat on the throne French adventurers and scientists carrying his flag traveled through large portions of what later became the United States of America and Canada.

Thanks to Henry, the fur trade began in North America. It was he, too, who began importing sturdy trees from North America and sent his fishing fleets to the rich banks off the coast of Newfoundland. Aware that other nations wanted to occupy North America, he also encouraged the settlement of the continent. Bonuses were paid to men willing to make their homes in America, and the crown paid all of their expenses in crossing the Atlantic and establishing themselves in the New World. Far ahead of his time, Henry initiated policies that Great Britain, Holland and Spain did not copy for many decades.

Above all, Henry destroyed the old feudal system. Authority was centralized in the crown.

The nobles who had sought greater power were doomed to disappointment. All power was vested in the monarch, and in no one else. Nobles might own large estates, but the crown delegated its powers only to officeholders appointed by the King. Henry IV became the sole master of France.

His foreign policy was simple: he wanted peace. But he knew the kings of Spain and Austria, who were members of the Hapsburg family, were aggressive and greedy. And so he tried to contain their ambitions by making a series of alliances without going to war. The Protestant states were eager to become his allies in spite of his highly publicized conversion to Catholicism—another sign, it might be noted, that few in his own day accepted his change of faith at face value.

Henry became fully occupied on the diplomatic front, and in the eighteen-month period that followed the establishment of his capital in Paris, he signed treaties with England, Holland and Sweden, the three most prominent Protestant powers. Thereafter, through the years, he also signed treaties with the Protestant German states and Swiss cantons.

He needed strong Catholic support, too, if he hoped to achieve a permanent peace at home, which was his principal goal; and the friendship of Catholic nations was vital if he wanted to contain the ambitions of Spain and Austria. Two of the more prominent Italian states, Tuscany and Venice, were pleased to become his allies in 1596 and 1597. As a supposed Catholic, he required the open support and recognition of the Vatican, and he paid a high price for it.

The Pope granted him an annulment of his marriage to Margaret, and in 1600 he married Marie de Médicis, daughter of the Grand Duke of Tuscany and a relative of Catherine de Médicis, his old enemy. He had seven children with Marie, the eldest of whom eventually became King Louis XIII. He found it impossible, however, to trust a wife who had the de Médicis name, and the marriage was not a happy one.

But Henry's sacrifice was not in vain. In 1601 he signed a treaty with Pope Paul V, and France became the formal ally of the Vatican. In later years Savoy and Lorraine also joined this alliance.

Throughout the better part of the period from 1600 to 1610 King Henry devoted most of his time and talents to internal matters. France became the wealthiest and most powerful nation on the continent of Europe. Henry never lost his sympathy for the common people, and the lowest of his subjects were free to approach him at any time to discuss their problems and grievances. In effect he made himself a court of last resort, and his subjects could appeal to him in person if they believed that the judges of the high courts had ruled against them unfairly.

In 1606 Henry suffered a severe personal blow when he discovered that Marshal Biron, one of his closest friends and seemingly loyal supporter, was conspiring against him. The plot was found out in time, and the King's life was saved. A ruthless man who lived in a cold-blooded age, Henry did not hesitate before condemning Biron to death.

In the main, Henry achieved most of his goals. There is no question that the lot of the peasant, the backbone of French society, improved dramatically. Thanks to the King, the export

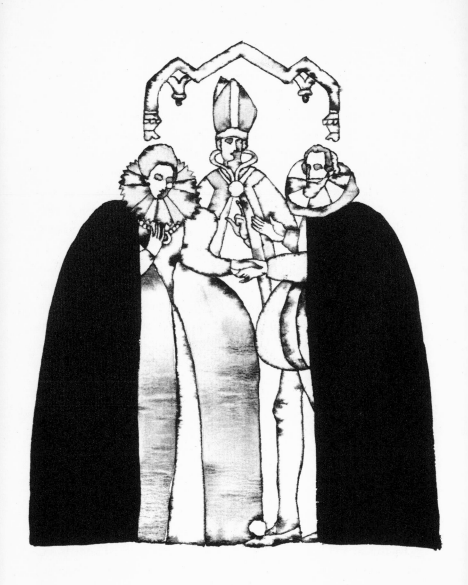

of grain was legalized, which afforded the poor farmers a better and larger market for their produce. They became prosperous, and before Henry's death there was "a chicken in the pot" on the dining table of every French household. Henry's foes had mocked him when he had proclaimed this as one of his goals, but, as was his custom, he enjoyed the last laugh.

The menace of Spain and Austria continued to hover over France, although the Hapsburgs could no longer use religion as an excuse to make war. They wanted part of the territory of wealthy, growing France, and year by year made less effort to mask their ambitions. Henry wanted peace, but could not ignore the threat to his country. Finally, late in 1609, he received solid evidence that they were secretly mobilizing against him.

He decided, reluctantly, that he had no choice but to strike the first blow. He declared war against them and sent his well-disciplined, superbly trained regiments across the Spanish border. In the months that followed he frantically organized the entire country for a concerted war effort.

Then, suddenly, in 1610, Henry was killed by an assassin who plunged a knife into his heart. How the man managed to reach the side of the King in his own well-guarded palace is a mystery. There are also conflicting reports regarding the killer. According to one persisting story, he was a madman. Another says that he was a secret agent in the pay of Austria and France. A third claims that the murderer was an ardent Catholic who believed Henry was a menace to Catholicism. A fourth insists that the assassin was a dedicated Huguenot who believed the King was a danger to Protestantism.

In a sense, Henry's death is proof of his greatest accomplishment: the establishment of religious freedom and the creation of a spirit of tolerance among his subjects. It is ironic that his killer was said by some to be a Catholic, and by others to be a Huguenot. All men of reason and good will mourned the death of one of history's greatest men.

Now, having learned the background and setting of the Edict of Nantes, the time has come to examine in greater detail the events that led to the proclamation of this extraordinary document.

5

The Crucible:
Was Religious Freedom a Myth?

THE Huguenots of France, from the great lords to the insignificant townsmen and peasants, automatically expected Henry IV to improve their lot once he became monarch of all France. They realized, of course, that he could do nothing until he made Paris his capital; but when he moved into the city in 1594, many expected miracles.

His Protestant generals urged him to act at once, and the hot-blooded Montmorency was the most insistent. But two men, Sully and Montauban, advised the King to exercise patience. The granting of equality to Huguenots, an unprecedented move, was certain to cause repercussions. Therefore, Sully and Montauban said, he would be wise to establish a solid basis before taking this radical step.

Henry decided their counsel was sound. The persecution of Huguenots had stopped immediately in each portion of France that he had occupied. But the granting of *legal* rights to a religious minority was another matter. His enemies might seize the excuse to renew the wars of religion in the hope of driving

him from the throne. Henry had often demonstrated his bold-
ness, but he knew that some circumstances required the exercise
of caution. This was one of them, and he forced himself to
wait.

His first move was obvious: he had to consolidate all power
in the crown. This he did, to the consternation of both Protestant and Catholic nobles who had hoped that their own feudal
powers would be restored to them. Several of the most influential men in the country had not yet sworn fealty to the King,
and when he assumed many of the prerogatives that dukes,
counts and barons had enjoyed for centuries, they became even
more hesitant.

The most prominent of those who dragged their feet was
Philippe-Emmanuel, Duc de Mercoeur, who was the governor
of the large province of Britanny. Mercoeur's opposition to the
King was doubly important because his wife, Marie, was
Duchess of Luxembourg and Penthièvre in her own right.
Between them they controlled a vast territory.

Mercoeur claimed he could not swear allegiance to the King
until he could determine to his own satisfaction that Henry's
conversion to Catholicism had been sincere. Henry, knowing
that the Duke was merely stalling, sent him an ultimatum:
submit or face the consequences. Mercoeur, who foolishly
believed the King was too busy to make good his threat, ignored
the message.

Henry promptly gathered several of his best infantry regiments, his most audacious squadrons of cavalry, and his finest
batteries of artillery. Riding at the head of the long column,
he set out from Paris for Britanny.

He did not need a corps of that size and strength to subdue Mercoeur, and he knew it. But he also realized that several lesser dukes, as well as a number of counts and barons, were waiting to see what would happen in Britanny. If Mercoeur should prove successful in his efforts to defy the crown, others would follow his example, and there would be rebellions all over France. Henry was determined to trample on Mercoeur so heavily that the others who were hesitating would swear their allegiance to him without delay.

Mercoeur sent a battalion of his own domestic troops to the border of Britanny. But these soldiers wisely put up no opposition when they saw the King's legions. Far more afraid of Henry than they were of Mercoeur, they feared they would be hanged as traitors if they fought Henry's men. The entire battalion, officers and men, not only surrendered to the advance guard, but begged permission to join Henry themselves. Their request was granted, of course.

Mercoeur realized it was useless to hold out and sued for peace. Henry refused to negotiate with him until the Duke swore fealty to him, and this the humbled Mercoeur did. Henry, instead of fining and dismissing him as some of the generals wanted, reappointed him Governor of Britanny.

The other nobles who had been holding out hastened to submit to the King.

By the end of 1596 Henry had made remarkable progress in consolidating his position. All tax collectors reported to the crown and sent their funds directly to the royal treasury, where Sully was in charge. He also received direct payments from the custom guards at the borders; this marked the first time that the dukes of the various provinces did not share in the customs revenues. Judges of the law courts were appointed by the King, and appeals were heard in royal courts, too. For hundreds of years appeals had been heard by princes and dukes, but now they lost these privileges.

The nobles, Catholic and Protestant alike, were helpless as they watched their rights vanish. No noble and no combination of nobles had the strength to stand up to Henry. The King's army would crush anyone in the realm who opposed him, and the nobles knew it.

Their only chance of regaining power lay in the granting of rights to Huguenots. With luck they might be able to snatch some of those basic rights themselves. And so, by the end of 1596, both Protestants and Catholics were asking the King to grant legal rights to the Huguenots.

Even the bishops joined in the requests for they had lost more than the nobles. Their revenues were no longer sent directly to the Vatican, but went instead to the royal treasury, and Henry decided what would be sent on to Rome. In fact, royal tax collecters appointed to each archdiocese and diocese supervised the collection of Church moneys from the faithful. Not even a cardinal dared to put aside for his own use more than Henry allowed.

The cardinals and bishops hoped that a decree granting rights to the Protestants would be worded in a way that would protect their own rights. They were miserable, and their plight was complicated by the attitude of the younger priests. Since the King appointed new bishops, a priest who wanted advancement made certain he stood in Henry's favor. As many dis-

covered, there was no better way to win Henry's gratitude than to report that a cardinal or bishop was not observing royal decrees to the letter. Rather than risk the King's disfavor, the cardinals and bishops made certain they observed royal regulations, but they chafed under the unfamiliar restrictions imposed on them.

By the beginning of 1597, however, Henry's control was so complete that he was ready to begin work on his Edict of Nantes. His own aim was simple: he wanted to grant guarantees of freedom of worship to Protestants without diminishing or otherwise harming the similar rights that Catholics already enjoyed. The very idea was unique. Nowhere in Europe were men of different faiths living side by side as equals. A truly revolutionary concept was on the verge of being developed in France.

It is true that Henry, remembering the long religious wars and the St. Bartholomew's Day Massacre, wanted greater rights given to the Huguenots. In the past three hundred and seventy years, however, he often has been portrayed by romantics as a crusader for religious tolerance. But that portrait is inaccurate and misleading. His ultimate goal was the achievement of domestic peace. France, he knew, would become a great nation only if her civil wars halted for all time. He also believed it essential that all authority be vested in the crown. The granting of rights to the Huguenots would achieve these ends.

After discussing the matter at length with his counselors, Henry issued a brief proclamation on February 2, 1597, announcing the formation of a commission to draw up a plan for an edict. Unfortunately, no copies of the proclamation itself are still in existence. Historians know that Henry issued it because of the numerous references to it in the correspondence and diaries of others. In fact, Sully, the financial and administrative expert who served his master with single-minded devotion for many years, claimed in his *Journal,* written after Henry's death, that he had been the author of the proclamation.

Regardless of who wrote the announcement, Henry was responsible for it and for setting the machinery in motion. From the outset he made it plain that he wanted and expected solid results. As chairman of the commission he appointed his Chancellor, Philippe de Montauban. The principal legal officer of the realm was hard-headed, competent and a member of an exceptionally devout Huguenot family. Although Montauban never lost sight of the King's interests and goals, he certainly was determined to obtain for his fellow Protestants the rights they were being denied.

As vice-chairman of the commission, Henry named Jean Jeannin, President of the Parliament of Normandy. In other words, Jeannin was chief justice of the highest law court in the province of Normandy. A tall, grim-faced man who supposedly had no sense of humor, Jeannin was a distinguished jurist and an ardent Roman Catholic. He was also a great patriot, having been one of the first Catholics of importance in France to cast his lot with Henry IV. This loyalty probably meant more to the King than Jeannin's other qualifications and must have been responsible, in large part, for his appointment.

The full commission was comprised of many other members, some of whom served full time, some part time. At one period or another, virtually all members of Henry's royal Council of

State sat in on at least some of the commission's meetings. The records indicate that approximately thirty Catholic and thirty Huguenot noblemen were commissioners, too. Whether all served at the same time or whether relatively small groups succeeded one another is not known.

A dozen Catholic bishops and priests were commissioners, as were an equal number of Protestant clergymen. According to Sully's *Journal,* the priests and ministers were the only members who were inclined to quarrel. Everyone else worked together in harmony, but the clergymen on both sides appear to have felt the need to act as champions of their respective causes.

Henry created a precedent by appointing a number of commoners, both Huguenot and Catholic, to the commission. This was the first time in the history of the nation that ordinary people—farmers, carpenters and fishermen—had been granted a voice in the creation of a national policy that would leave an indelible impression on every Frenchman. To claim, however, that Henry was in any way motivated by a desire to inaugurate a "democratic" regime would be absurd.

Other rulers, Elizabeth of England or Philip of Spain, for example, may have been horrified by his gesture, but it must be remembered that he had firmly consolidated all power in the hands of one person, the monarch. Henry, with the instinctive shrewdness of genius, was doing no more than placating the common people, his subjects. By allowing a handful of their number to sit on the commission, he was helping to ensure the obedience of all his subjects to the edict the commission would prepare.

The people did not elect these delegates. They were appointed by the crown, and Henry, who took no unnecessary risks in governing his people, undoubtedly made certain that the ordinary folk who attended the meetings of the commission would accept the decisions of their superiors. These commoners were given no voting rights on the commission. Their living expenses were paid by the crown during the many months of deliberation, and they probably received wages as well. They had the right to attend all meetings and to express their opinions freely, without fear of punishment if, for example, they disagreed with Montauban or Jeannin.

But it must be stressed that the function of the commoners was advisory. When deliberations were concluded on a given question and the clergymen, nobles and others of consequence cast their ballots, the ordinary men had no voting privileges. Even so, they made history by taking part in the discussions and debates.

The commission also included one final group, a number of Jesuit priests, who were hated and feared by all of their colleagues. Ever since their religious order had been founded, in 1534 by St. Ignatius Loyola, the Jesuits had been centers of controversy. All were intellectuals, perhaps the best-educated men of the age, and although the internal discipline of the Order was strong, they obeyed no one except their own superiors. This, of course, always annoyed the cardinals and bishops who had no authority over them.

The French Jesuits had been the first priests in the country to support Henry. They shared his goal of making the nation great, and they were afraid of no one, be it a Huguenot general, a Catholic bishop, or a high-ranking nobleman of either faith. The incomplete records of the commission make it impossible to determine how many Jesuits attended its sessions as members. There may have been as few as three or four or as many as a dozen or more.

Regardless of their number, the Jesuits were there as Henry's personal watchdogs. They shared his ambitions and ideals, and they intended to make certain that the document prepared by the commission reflected his views. They realized, as he did, that France would become the leading nation of Europe only if her civil wars stopped. As men who understood the mechanics of power, they approved of the way he took authority from the high nobles and clergy and added to his own.

Above all, the Jesuits were the first intellectual liberals to appear within the Roman Catholic Church. Although their own aim was the strengthening of Catholic faith, they realized that this goal could not be accomplished by the suppression of other religions. The persecution of Protestants in Catholic nations inevitably caused retaliation in such Protestant states as England, Sweden and the German principalities. The very appearance of Protestantism in the movement known as the Reformation had been caused by the heavy-handed wielding of authority by Church officials.

The granting of rights and privileges to other faiths, the Jesuits believed, was the best way to prevent the spread of Protestantism and to strengthen the Catholic Church. Only the most farsighted individual could share this view, and, in a bigoted age, the cardinals and bishops held contrary opinions. This difference in attitudes, combined with their inability to exercise discipline over the Jesuits, caused them to regard members of the Order with great distaste.

The Huguenots had no love for the Jesuits, either, although they had no specific cause for complaint. It was impossible, of course, for the Protestants to forget that members of the Order were priests. And there was something mysterious about the Jesuits. They always dressed in somber black, seemed to spend all their spare time reading, and, above all, kept their own counsel. They mixed with no outsiders and made no attempt to find friends outside their own ranks. Knowing little about them and understanding still less, the Huguenots were inclined to regard them with suspicion. There was even a rumor—although false—that the Jesuits had been responsible for the St. Bartholomew's Day Massacre.

Almost everyone who attended the sessions of the commission complained bitterly about the presence of the Jesuits. Sully wrote in his *Journal* that they were "deceitful and mean," but offered no proof of his charges. Several of the bishops banded together and sent a request to the Vatican that the Jesuits be ordered by their own superiors to leave the commission. Nothing whatever came of the request. Similarly, some of the Huguenot nobles wrote to the Duc de Montmorency, who was now Constable of France, the second-ranking man in the nation, asking him to use his influence to have the Jesuits withdrawn.

It is unknown whether Montmorency heeded the request. If he went to the King, Henry turned him down. But it is more likely that the Constable already knew his master's attitude and made no attempt to influence him. Everyone close to Henry knew he placed great trust in the Jesuits.

Events outside the suite of rooms in the Louvre where the commission held its meetings in 1597 proved that the Kings faith was justified. A sudden international crisis gripped France: an unexpected Spanish invasion. Henry was forced to leave Paris to go into the field with his army. At the very least, the work of the commission would have been postponed had the Jesuits not proved completely loyal to the aims of the King. They represented him, reporting to him regularly, and their steadfastness enabled the great work to continue.

6

The Crisis

THE commission appointed to draw up the terms of what was known at the Louvre as the "Huguenot Edict" met daily, and King Henry IV made it his business to spend at least a portion of each morning or afternoon at its sessions. In this way he dramatized how important its deliberations were to him; anyone familiar with the state of affairs in the nation realized how valuable his time had become.

France, as everyone in the King's immediate circle well knew, was in trouble. It might be argued that Henry's ambitions were responsible, for he was trying to expand in many directions at the same time. Roads, bridges and canals were being built, shipwrights were constructing the largest navy in French history, and new industries were being encouraged. Farmers were granted special privileges so that they would grow crops for export, and expeditions were being sent to the New World.

The treasury could not stand the strain of so much activity. Sully had not yet perfected what would become the most efficient system of tax collection in the world, and funds were inadequate to meet all of the heavy expenses. Henry had to spend most of his time dealing with financial problems. Hating to be in debt to anyone, he resisted the suggestions of Sully and others that he borrow substantial sums from wealthier nations. Representatives of the Vatican hinted that the Catholic Church would be pleased to advance him whatever he needed, but he suspected a trap and rejected the offer. If he allowed the Vatican to gain even partial control of his purse strings, it would be doubly difficult for him to grant new liberties to Protestants.

The agents of Philip II were aware of Henry's difficulties, too, and the Spanish monarch persuaded himself that Henry was too poor to pay the cost of maintaining a large army in the field. The time was ripe to get rid of the most dangerous of his foes on the Continent, Philip concluded, and he secretly prepared to launch a major operation.

One night in mid-March, 1597, Henry was attending a party at the Tuileries, the palace that was the official residence of his sister, Princess Catherine. The affair was interrupted by the arrival of a courier, his boots and cloak heavily covered with dust. The guests were horrified to learn that a strong column of Spanish infantry, cavalry and artillery had marched into France from Belgium, a Spanish possession, and was attacking the fortified city of Amiens.

Henry's reaction was immediate. "I have played the King of France long enough!" he declared. "It is time I return to the King of Navarre!"

The garrisons in the vicinity of Paris were alerted, and before dawn Henry marched off to war at the head of six regiments of cavalry and three of infantry. Montmorency accompanied him as second-in-command. Orders were sent to other garrisons to march on Amiens, and Biron was given the unenviable task of raising additional regiments, principally from the ranks of veterans who had retired when the civil wars had ended.

Before Henry left Paris, he learned the nasty truth from Sully: the royal treasury was almost empty. The King promptly placed his private fortune at his treasurer's disposal, and in another of his famous statements declared, "I would rather be a begger King than a wealthy exile."

Princess Catherine set an example for the ladies of France by donating her jewels and gold trinkets to the cause. Duchesses and countesses did the same. Collections were taken in Catholic churches and the few in which Huguenots were permitted to worship. Merchants and peasants voluntarily made offers, and the members of four newly raised regiments said they would accept no wages for a period of four months.

The entire French nation responded to the crisis. Henry was right when he said that Philip made the task of unifying the country far easier. Men everywhere devoted themselves to the single objective of defeating the enemy.

There was one notable exception. At Henry's express command, the commission working on the "Huguenot Edict" continued to meet. Nothing, the King instructed, was to be allowed to interfere with its deliberations.

Henry himself had to subordinate everything else to the task of repelling the invaders. If Amiens fell, Spanish troops could spread out across northern France, and Paris itself would be menaced.

The King's worst fears were realized when he reached Amiens. Less than twenty-four hours earlier the city had fallen, and the banner of Philip was flying from the ramparts. But the Spaniards had not yet had an opportunity to consolidate their victory, and Henry reacted swiftly. Giving the enemy no chance to use Amiens as a base of operations, he posted his regiments around it and put it under siege. Gradually, in the days and weeks that followed, the arrival of reinforcements enabled him to strengthen his ring around Amiens.

If he could force the invaders to surrender, Philip's campaign would collapse; but if the captors of the city could hold out long enough, additional troops could be dispatched from Belgium. It was even possible that the Spaniards might open a second front in the south by sending another expedition across the Pyrenees Mountains. Although the latter move was fairly remote, the French could take no chances and stationed strong defense forces in Navarre.

Henry took personal charge of the siege of Amiens. He not only directed the strategy of the campaign, but risked his life repeatedly by leading cavalry charges against the city's walls. His reason, he told his aides who protested that he had no right to behave so recklessly, was simple: he wanted to inspire his troops.

Forgetting that he was no longer young, he spent long hours in the saddle and longer at the war council table. Once again, he was not like other men, and his energy seemed boundless. Then, one day in early April, he collapsed and was sent to bed by his physicians. He was suffering from what would be known in a later period as nervous exhaustion.

But he would not relinquish command of the corps to Montmorency and continued to direct the campaign from his sickbed. During this period, with the fate of France at stake, he concerned himself with only one other matter: the deliberations of the commission in Paris.

The value to Henry of the Jesuit members became apparent. Each day without fail, a Jesuit commissioner appeared at the camp before Amiens and was admitted to the King's tent for a private discussion. No one down to the present day knows what was said at these meetings. No records were kept, no notes taken. The priest-courier reported the latest developments to Henry and discussed the situation with him. Then, after receiving fresh instructions and resting for a few hours, the Jesuit started back to Paris.

The messengers were so punctual that members of the King's personal staff came to expect their arrival soon after midday dinner. The Jesuits rarely disappointed them. Their loyalty to Henry was as unflagging as his trust in them was complete.

Others in the French camp were dismayed. Montmorency, in his only known dispute with the King, told everyone who would listen to him that Jesuits were the most two-faced of all Papists. High-ranking French Catholics, although a trifle more discreet, were equally uncomplimentary. But Henry went on his own way, ignored the abuse, and continued to put his faith in the Jesuits.

Their reports were giving him great concern. The deliberations, they told him, had degenerated into senseless bickering and name-calling. Henry roused himself from his lethargy and sent orders to Paris instructing the commissioners to get on with their task. But they continued to quarrel, and neither faction would listen to the Jesuits, who tried to conciliate both sides.

Meanwhile the military situation at Amiens grew more threatening. A Spanish relief column heavily laden with supplies for the garrison broke through the French cordon. The next day, seventeen hours too late, Biron arrived in Henry's camp with five fresh regiments. The reinforcements were welcome, of course, but the corps was still not strong enough to reduce the augmented garrison. Henry, still in bed, conducted a council of war in his tent, and was forced to agree with his generals, who believed the siege might go on for months.

Still more troops were needed and fresh funds had to be raised for military wages, provisions and arms. It dawned on Henry that Philip of Spain was even more shrewd and clever than he had realized. The Spaniard, knowing the French treasury was almost bankrupt, was using Amiens to bleed his foes of all they still possessed. If he succeeded, conditions in France would become so chaotic that the people might revolt.

While Henry pondered his course, he received word of a fresh catastrophe. A Jesuit arrived at his camp with word that the deliberations of the commission had broken down. Montauban and Jeannin were no longer able to maintain order, and although members of the commission remained at the Louvre, their meetings had been suspended.

Henry knew that he alone could handle both situations. Ignoring the advice of the physicians who told him not to leave his bed, he placed Montmorency in command at Amiens and returned to Paris. According to legend, he was so weak on this journey that he had to be strapped to his saddle to prevent him from toppling into the dusty road.

When the King arrived in Paris he summoned the magistrates of the city and requested them to raise money. Then he called in members of his "Huguenot Commission," but before he could address them he collapsed and fell unconscious. A week passed before the physicians pronounced him out of immediate danger.

The medical profession was in charge now and, supported by the members of Henry's family, sent the King off to his nearby country château of Saint-Germain to recuperate. Montmorency returned to Paris to take charge of affairs of state, and Biron assumed command of the army at Amiens.

By the end of May Henry was sufficiently recovered to confer for a morning with the Constable, who returned to Paris with word for all that there would be action in the immediate future. The following day Sully was summoned to Saint-Germain, and Henry gave him instructions that inaugurated a new, revolutionary method of obtaining funds.

All members of the nobility were landowners. Under the terms of a simple decree signed by Henry, every noble was required to pay taxes on the land he owned. The Roman Catholic Church, as such, was specifically exempted from the decree. But cardinals, bishops and many lower members of the priesthood were property owners, and in that capacity they were required to pay the new taxes, too.

The nobles and clergy protested in vain. Squads of troops accompanied the tax collectors who fanned out through all of

France, and it was evident that the King meant business. Not even the greatest lord wanted to be arrested and tried on charges of treason, and gold began to pour in to the royal treasury. Almost overnight the nation became solvent again.

Then it was the turn of the "Huguenot Commission." Montauban and Jeannin were summoned to Saint-Germain, and the King made his position plain. He wanted results, at once. Any member of the commission who balked or failed to cooperate with his colleagues would be relieved. Then, no matter what his station, he would be sent to prison for obstructing royal justice. The threat applied equally to dukes, bishops and commoners.

The commission went to work in earnest, the tax collectors were busy, and the Duc de Mayenne, head of the House of Guise, demonstrated his loyalty to the crown by marching to Amiens with the legions of Lorraine. There, in spite of his three hundred pounds, the luxury-loving Mayenne slept in a soldier's tent and actually led his cavalry in forays against the enemy.

By the early part of August the physicians allowed Henry to return to Paris. He celebrated by taking the chair at the meetings of the commission and insisting that the work be speeded. Unfortunately, he remained in Paris for only a few days. A courier brought the unwelcome news that the Hapsburg rulers of Austria were coming to the aid of their Spanish relatives and had dispatched an army of twenty thousand men to France. This force, the messenger said, was marching rapidly across Europe toward Amiens.

The information appeared accurate, and Henry realized the war with Spain had reached a climactic phase. Ordering all available reserves in every part of France to proceed at once to Amiens, he returned there himself to resume personal command of the siege. Again the necessities of war made it impossible for him to force his subordinates on the "Huguenot Commission" to hammer out a satisfactory, immediate agreement.

The King reached Amiens in mid-August and lost no time tightening the noose around the Spanish garrison there. French patrols were doubled, making it virtually impossible for even a messenger to get in or out of the besieged city. During the next weeks small units of French reinforcements arrived, sometimes in battalion strength, sometimes in small companies. Henry put the men to work digging trenches and prepared feverishly for the Austrians, who were expected in October.

But the Austrian army surprised the French by arriving unexpectedly on September 15th. Mayenne was the general on duty at the time the enemy vanguard appeared, and he showed remarkable poise. Riding to the scene of the action, he ordered the French artillery to open a heavy bombardment.

Henry, acting on the advice of his physicians, had gone at dawn with a few companions for a day of hunting in the forest to the west of Amiens. The sounds of the furious artillery fire in the distance made him realize that something out of the ordinary was taking place, and he rode hard for the scene of action.

By the time he arrived, shortly after noon, his army was engaged in a full-scale battle with the Austrians. A major part of the French force was caught between the newly arrived reinforcements and the Spanish defenders inside Amiens. Compelled to take up defensive positions, the French were crouching behind the breastworks in their trenches, trying to hold firm.

Henry realized that they were such good targets for the foe that they would suffer crippling losses unless there was an immediate change of tactics. And so, taking command himself, he brought up his reserves to keep the Spaniards busy and sent his main force forward in a full-scale counterattack against the Austrians.

The battle continued through the rest of the day and evening, with the French gradually gaining the upper hand. The Austrians were veterans, but never had they met such determined enemies, and by nine o'clock that night they were in full retreat. Before midnight they had started the long march back to their own land, their proud regiments shattered. The defenders of Amiens once again faced the French alone.

Philip of Spain may have been a tyrant, but he was intelligent enough to know when he had been defeated. When messengers brought word of the Austrian defeat to Madrid, he sent orders to the commander at Amiens to surrender the garrison. The gates of the city opened on September 25th, and the long campaign came to an end.

There was no immediate victory celebration in the French camp, as everyone was too weary. But even the most ignorant, illiterate foot soldier knew that Philip had lost his greatest gamble. There would be real peace at last between France and Spain, and in time a firm treaty would be signed.

Henry spent twenty-four hours visiting the wounded in his army and inspecting the damage done at Amiens. Then, after going off for the day's hunting trip that the battle with the Austrians had denied him, he was ready to concentrate on his

next major task. With a solid peace assured and his treasury solvent, he could devote himself to the problem of working out a fair solution of the Huguenot problem.

Unwilling to let the matter wait until he and his victorious army marched back to Paris, he sat down in his tent and, in his own hand, wrote a letter to Montauban and Jeannin. It is one of the few communications by Henry that has been preserved in full and may be found in the National Library in Paris today. The most important portions read:

"Long and patiently have we awaited the dispensation of justice to our loyal Huguenot subjects. Long before the interminable siege of Amiens was undertaken by our recently defeated foes, we gave the trust for the solution of this vexing matter into the hands of gentlemen who, we believed, would bring this matter to an end with dispatch. Now Amiens has been recovered and the external foe driven from our soil, but the Huguenots of France still cry out in vain for relief.

"We find this situation intolerable.

"We know, from our own experience, the frustrations and inconveniences visited upon those who profess the New Faith, and our heart goes out to those who suffer for no reason other than their sincere and honorable faith in God.

"The very laws of France . . . are a mummery unworthy of the talents of an inferior court jester. Permit us to call your attention, milords, to only one of them, which specifies that none who profess the New Faith may hold public office in our realm.

"Thus it is that, under a strict interpretation of the law, even our Constable, Henry, Duc de Montmorency, holds his post of highest trust illegally! Fortunately for France, we have elected to ignore this most ludicrous decree, promulgated by a predecessor lacking in both wisdom and compassion.

"Rather than repeal this decree, and with it, individually, many another, we have chosen to treat with the matter in a single document that deals with all aspects of the religious situation in the realm. It is our continuing conviction . . . that the problem should be dealt with . . . in this manner. . . .

"But now our patience is exhausted, and our spirit, long perturbed, is not yet at rest. For the good of our people, to whom all of our efforts are devoted, we require such tranquility, and are determined that it shall be achieved.

"Therefore we do direct and enjoin the gentlemen charged with our responsibility in this Huguenot matter to conclude their deliberations with all due dispatch, not allowing haste to make a mockery of their efforts. We direct that the final documents which will for all time settle this dilemma be submitted to us for our approval, signature and application of our Great Seal three months hence, from this date."

Henry had set a deadline, and the commission was ordered to complete its work by December 27, 1597. His letter made no mention of what would happen if his commands were not obeyed, but it was unnecessary for him to spell out a threat. Every commissioner knew that, at the very least, he would be dismissed from office and banished from the King's court. But Henry could do far more than disgrace an official whose efforts did not please him. The offender's property could be taken from him and appropriated by the crown. And although it was unlikely that Montauban and Jeannin and the nobles and bishops would be sent to prison, the possibility could not be discounted.

The commissioners, conscious of the gravity of their own personal positions, went to work in earnest. At last the document that would be known as the Edict of Nantes began to take shape.

7

A Blueprint for Tolerance

It was neither laziness nor a lack of good will on the part of the "Huguenot Commissioners" that had caused so many delays in the preparation of the edict demanded by King Henry IV. Montauban and Jeannin sincerely believed in their monarch's cause, and so did many other members of the group. Their trouble, basically, was that they literally did not know where to begin or how to proceed. Never, in all human history, had there been a document that granted specific rights and privileges to a religious minority. Lacking precedents, the commission floundered, made innumerable false moves, and had to start again at the beginning.

When the commissioners returned to their labors in the autumn of 1597, they took a completely new approach. The question of providing for guarantees to the Huguenots without infringing on the already-existing rights of the Catholic majority was divided into four subsections: religious, civil, legal and military. In each of these fields there were specific problems to be solved.

93

The most pressing ones, obviously, were religious. Under the present law, Protestant worship services were forbidden everywhere in France. Permission had to be granted to the Huguenots to hold services. Should this right be unrestricted? The Catholic cardinals and bishops protested that it would be unfair to grant such rights in exclusively Catholic towns. And Cardinal de Bourbon, the King's cousin, who was cardinal-archbishop of Paris, insisted it would be an insult to permit the building of Protestant churches in the capital. He was so firm on the point, being supported by the Vatican in the matter, that the edict itself was threatened.

The commission, while trying to hammer out a solution, turned next to civil matters. Here, thanks to King Henry's adament stand, there was relatively little argument. Although some of the Catholics wanted to keep the Huguenots in the category of second-class citizens, the King had made it clear, repeatedly, that he would tolerate no such trickery.

So the commissioners decided, after a short debate, that the Huguenots would be granted full rights of citizenship. It is significant that the vote in favor of this stand was unanimous. No commissioner, regardless of how high his rank, wanted to arouse Henry's ire by taking a position which he was known to oppose with all his being.

The legal question was one of the most complicated the commission faced. Inevitably, there would be disputes between Catholics and Protestants. Special machinery would be needed to handle these problems. Montauban and Jeannin, themselves lawyers, worked out the matter in a way that seemed fair to everyone. Special courts would be created to deal with the legal questions, its members to be appointed by the crown. Both Catholic and Protestant magistrates would sit on these courts.

Montauban and Jeannin proposed that each court be comprised of Catholics and Huguenots in equal numbers. The Catholic clergymen, supported by some of the Catholic nobles, protested. Since Catholicism was the religion of the French majority, they argued, Catholics should be granted a majority of the seats on each court. All of the Huguenots on the commission fought this proposal vehemently. A Catholic majority, they declared, would rule in favor of fellow Catholics in any law suit; a Protestant minority would be powerless, and justice would become a sham.

The military problem was equally vexing. In some communities, particularly in the south of France near Navarre, virtually the entire population was Protestant. This was true, for example, in the town of Montauban, Chancellor Philippe's home. The people of these communities, remembering the raids and military suppression of the past by crown troops, wanted the right to defend themselves. They wanted new, high walls and towers, artillery and other weapons. Above all, they wanted the cost of their garrisons to be paid by the crown, a privilege that fortified Catholic towns had long enjoyed.

Many of the Catholics on the commission were outraged by this proposal. The nobles, in particular, were upset, claiming that as the nation's principal taxpayers, they saw no reason why they should be forced to pay for the defense of Protestant towns. The debates on the matter became so heated that the commission appeared on the verge of dissolution. Only the skill of Montauban and Jeannin—and the ever-present threat of the

King's displeasure—prevented commissioners on both sides from stalking out of the meetings.

One additional problem that was placed in no specific category proved very hard to solve. As we have already seen, such higher-ranking Catholic clergymen as cardinals, bishops and abbots were nominated by the crown and confirmed by the pope. This gave the ruling monarch a strong hold over the clergy, but Henry had quietly expanded even that influence during the previous year. In a move made without publicity, he had proposed to Rome that the crown also pay the wages of all Catholic clergymen in France.

The Vatican, stunned by this display of seeming generosity, had been quick to agree. Not until too late had Rome realized the full significance of the maneuver. Henry had obtained a stranglehold on the Catholic clergy, and could cut off the income of any priest who spoke or acted in a manner contrary to the interests of the crown.

News of the King's move had seeped out during the preceding months, and the rank and file of Protestants were clamoring for the same privilege. The day was at hand when they would have their own churches, congregations and ministers. Therefore they wanted the royal treasury to pay the wages of their clergymen, too. This, they argued, was far preferable to contributing from their own pockets for the purpose.

The Catholic nobles on the commission protested when the suggestion was made, but the bishops argued in favor of the plan. Themselves hobbled, they wanted to see members of the Huguenot clergy similarly trussed.

Montauban and the other Protestants on the commission recognized the dangers inherent in permitting the crown to pay the wages of their ministers. But they felt the risk was worth taking, principally because the demand by the Protestant layman was so vehement. Inasmuch as each Huguenot clergyman worked independently, rather than through a hierarchy like that of the Catholics, it was felt that the power of the crown over the individual Huguenot minister would not be too great.

A very few Protestants on the commission, looking into the future were aware of a subtle, long-range risk. No one quite believed that Henry's conversion to Catholicism had been sincere, and in any event, he was sympathetic to the Huguenots. Therefore it was unlikely that he would do anything to harm their interests. But the day might come when another monarch sitting on the French throne would be less friendly to the Protestants. Such a king, if he chose, could force the Huguenot clergy to obey his will by threatening to stop paying their wages. And the very lack of a Protestant hierarchy would make it doubly difficult for a minister to hold out against the crown. An individual clergyman, supported merely by his own conscience and, to an extent, by his congregation, would not find it an easy matter to defy the might and majesty of the French crown.

The matter was aired without hesitation at the meetings of the commission. Here was another case in which the Catholic clergy seemed to be acting in favor of the Huguenots, who, in turn, appeared opposed to their own interests. In any event, the issue was never in doubt. The demand by Huguenots in every part of France was so great that the people would have appealed to King Henry for a reversal of the ruling it had been decided that the Protestant ministers would not be paid their wages by the royal treasury.

Perhaps the most bitter fight in the commission centered on the subject of education. All universities in France were Catholic. Each of the cardinal-archbishops had a college or university under his jurisdiction, reporting directly to him. Most faculty members were Catholic clergymen, and only at the Sorbonne, in Paris, were there a few laymen who were instructors.

There were no Huguenot universities in the country. The founding of a new school of higher education was regarded as an enormous, complicated undertaking, and so no one even thought in terms of opening a new Protestant university in France. It should be remembered that theology and philosophy were two of the primary subjects studied at virtually every European university during the age of Henry IV, and so institutions of higher learning were, in a sense, seminaries for clergymen. Therefore it is easy to understand why the Huguenots, who as yet had no legal rights and no religious freedoms, were not yet thinking in terms of opening their own university.

In essence, the problem was simple: the universities of France were not only operated *by* Catholics, but *for* Catholics. No Protestant or Jewish students were admitted.

The wealthier Huguenot nobles were not disturbed by these restrictions. Their sons were sent, as Henry himself had been, to Protestant universities in Switzerland, England or Sweden. But the sons of the lesser nobles and the merchants could not afford to travel abroad for a higher education, and were denied the right to attend any French university.

The Huguenots on the commission argued that the right to attend an institute of higher learning was fundamental. The Catholics, particularly the clergy, retorted furiously that an education given at one of their universities was a privilege reserved for those of their own faith. Since it was a man's right to close the doors of his home to outsiders, they argued, they had the same prerogative in their universities.

It is significant that Montauban and Jeannin split only on this one issue. The Chancellor, realizing that the future of Protestantism in France depended upon the coming generations, demanded that promising young Huguenots be allowed to attend the universities. Jeannin, accepting the position of the bishops, fought just as hard for the exclusion of all but Catholic students.

Every issue of consequence had been thoroughly aired in the commission's chambers in the Louvre by the time that Henry returned to Paris in early November, 1597, at the head of his victorious army. The King led his troops in a triumphal parade through the streets of his cheering capital, and a two-day holiday was declared. The nobles gave banquets and balls; special services of thanksgiving were held at Notre Dame, Cardinal de Bourbon's cathedral; fireworks displays amused the people; and thousands literally danced in the streets.

Henry, after being absent from the city for so long a time, made only token appearances at the banquets held in the Louvre. While others celebrated, he closeted himself with Sully and Montmorency to review the overall affairs of state. Then, although the "Huguenot Commission" had suspended its activities for two days, he summoned Montauban and Jeannin.

They gave him a report on the progress to date, and the King surprised them by making no comment. Indicating neither pleasure nor vexation, he heard all they had to say and then dismissed them. They were unable to guess his reaction.

A lesser monarch than Henry IV, having set a deadline for the completion of his commission's work, would have been content to wait until that date before taking further action. But Henry was too impatient, and the Huguenot-Catholic question was far too important to be allowed to drag on. And so, a day or two after the celebrations ended, the King astonished his commissioners by appearing in their council chamber just as they had convened for their morning session.

The King made a brief speech. The commissioners, he said, had done their work well. They had reduced the problem to a set of specific questions. All that remained now was to obtain equally specific, succinct solutions. He saw no need for continuing debate. The time had come, he declared, for the making of decisions, which he hoped would be unanimous. If there were any problems the commissioners could not decide, he would settle such matters himself.

Smiling but firm, Henry departed as abruptly as he had appeared.

The commissioners needed no further urging to cut short their deliberations. With the King demanding immediate action, votes were taken on every issue. Men who had been inclined to hold out for their own points of view were suddenly willing to compromise.

The voting was completed within a few more days, and the results were incorporated in a draft of the commission's findings.

This document, written by two men, was submitted to Henry within the week, and became the keystone of his Edict.

Ironically, virtually nothing is known about the pair who actually wrote the famous paper. One was a Catholic priest named Jean Melan, the other a Huguenot minister named Paul Broget. Melan was a secretary on the staff of Cardinal de Bourbon, and since such a post was given, as a rule, to young men of promise, it might be assumed that he was both young and bright. Broget, who became a French citizen because of the Edict, had served at one time as a chaplain on the staff of the Duc de Montmorency and was known as a "warrior-clergyman." Melan eventually became a *monseigneur* and held an administrative post in the Church hierarchy in Paris. Broget, some years later, was mentioned as the pastor of a Huguenot church in Bordeaux. Unfortunately, no other details are known about the lives of either, although they were the principal authors of what became the Edict of Nantes.

In any event, the commission's work was finished, and a complete document was submitted to Henry. In the days that followed, he closeted himself with Montauban and Jeannin, and together they made changes in the wording and perhaps in the substance of the decree. Since no copies of the original document prepared by Melan and Broget have survived, it is impossible to tell what they contributed or what was done by the King, Montauban and Jeannin.

Regardless of who wrote what portions of the document, the Edict was in final form by late November, 1597, more than a month prior to the deadline that Henry had set.

8

The Edict

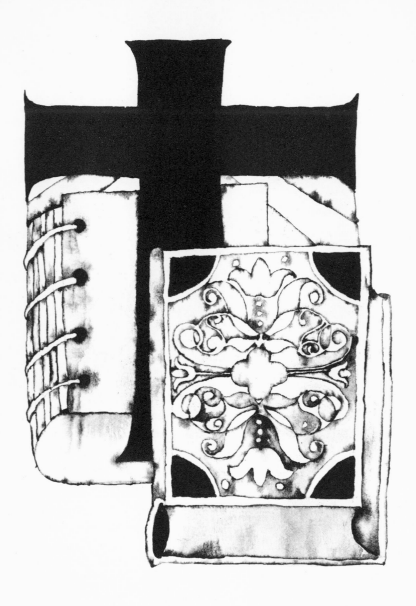

THE Edict of Nantes dealt with scores of specific matters, and in its final form was almost one hundred pages long. Its authors were concerned with specific problems, not literary style, and so the paper, as such, may be among the dullest of the great documents of history.

Only the first paragraph was inspiring: "We, Henry of France, the Fourth of that name, hereby grant complete liberty of conscience to all of our subjects not of the Roman Catholic, or majority, faith in our realm."

That one sentence established a new precedent for mankind. It meant that every Protestant in France had the right to worship God in his own way. A brief study of the wording will indicate, too, that it gave similar rights to the Jews of France. That, however, was purely theoretical. In practice, the Jews were not included, although they were no longer actively persecuted.

The Edict was drawn up to deal with the status of the Christian minority in France and was issued for that purpose.

Henry, by granting the Huguenots the right to worship God in their own way, put on paper a principle that never before had been enunciated.

This is not to say that there had never been religious tolerance in the world. The ancient Romans, for example, had cared nothing about a man's religion, their concern being solely political. Saul of Tarsus, a Jew who changed his name when he became a Christian and is known to posterity as St. Paul, was proud of his status as a full-fledged citizen of Rome. Going further back in history, the Hittites in 1200 B.C. permitted men to worship as they wished within the boundaries of their empire in Asia Minor.

Henry IV of France was the first to commit the principle of religious freedom to paper, the first to make into the law of his realm a man's right to worship as he pleased. It is the *legal* establishment of this principle, above all else, that makes the Edict of Nantes a unique document.

It is significant to note the part that this declaration played in the growth of that same principle in the New World, which has become the great bastion of religious freedom. Henry, as has already been noted, was very active in exploring and colonizing the New World. The French noblemen and priests, including Jesuits, who came to North America lived under the provisions of the Edict of Nantes. They brought its principles with them, and although the majority who eventually settled in New France were Catholic, complete freedom of religion was granted to all wherever the flag of France waved.

The Edict dealt with the question of public Protestant worship in a complicated manner. Huguenots were allowed to hold public worship services wherever they had held the right in 1576 and the early months of 1577, as well as in those places where the right had been granted in the Edict of Poitiers in 1577, the Treaty of Nérac of 1579, and the Treaty of Fleix in 1580. In order to ensure that there would be no quibbling on the matter, the Edict of Nantes carefully listed each town and village covered by these provisions.

Then the new Edict broke fresh ground. Protestant worship was permitted in public in any community where a majority of the citizens were Huguenots. It was also permitted in two towns of each *baillage* (or bailiwick, a unit that corresponds, roughly, to an English shire, that is, larger than an American county but smaller than an American state) in which the Protestants were in the minority. In all these places, the Huguenots were permitted to build churches or to buy existing buildings which they could transform into churches.

Cardinal de Bourbon won one important victory. The Huguenots were not allowed to conduct public worship services in Paris or its surroundings. Here the Protestants were granted a minor consolation. Previously they had been forbidden to hold public worship services in an area extending ten leagues (thirty miles) from the walls of the city. That area was reduced to five leagues (fifteen miles).

Special rights were granted to every *seigneur*, a noble who owned his own manor house. All such nobles who were Huguenots were granted the right to hold worship services under their own roofs. The major Protestant nobles were permitted to build churches on their estates and hold public worship services there. A minor *seigneur* was placed under mild restrictions: services for a maximum of thirty persons could be held in his manor house.

Anyone, noble or commoner or, for that matter, a congregation, was entitled to own the land and buildings on which Protestant churches were located. Neither land nor buildings could be taken from individuals for the payment of personal debts. Equally important, in a move that matched the rights granted to Catholics, all Huguenot church property and buildings were specifically excluded from taxation by the crown, by duchies, provinces or communities. In other words, the long-held Catholic right to own tax-exempt property used for religious purposes was extended to the Huguenots.

The granting of this right may appear relatively minor. But it, perhaps, of all the rights granted to the French Protestants, gave them stature in the eyes of ordinary citizens. Since no information is available, it is impossible to say whether the clause was developed and hammered out in the meetings of the commission or whether it was added later in the private conferences held by Henry, Montauban and Jeannin. If the bold, original thinking of King Henry in other matters is any criterion, it is possible that he himself was the originator of this provision. In any event, it accomplished a great deal in making the Huguenots appear respectable and legitimate in the eyes of the Catholic majority.

In the matter of civil rights, the Huguenots won a complete victory: they were granted full civil rights. These rights were spelled out in full. A Protestant could not be barred from any public office in the realm, royal or otherwise, on grounds of

religion. Specifically, every Huguenot had the opportunity to hold office.

Similarly, Huguenots were permitted to trade freely with all persons, both inside and outside France. They were also granted the right to inherit property.

Until then, both of these rights had been denied the Protestants. This had curbed the growth of a Huguenot middle class, since Protestant merchants had not been permitted to trade with other Frenchmen or with foreigners. It is interesting to note that in the years following the promulgation of the Edict of Nantes, a new Huguenot middle class came into being almost overnight. The appearance of this group was so sudden that only one conclusion can be drawn: Huguenots had been trading for years, but had been concealing their religion.

The right of Huguenots to inherit property was precious, too. Few changes took place in practice, however, since the right had been granted, unofficially, from the time that Henry had become King of France.

In the realm of education the Protestants won another sweeping victory. Enrollment in a French university was regarded, in the Edict of Nantes, as a full-fledged civil right. "No one," the document declared, "may be denied admittance to any university, college or school because of his faith. It is the civil right of any Huguenot to attend any university, college or school, including such institutions which are administered under the jurisdiction of the Roman Catholic Church."

This clause, more than any other, was resented by the Catholics of France, particularly the clergy. And, as will be seen in a later chapter, it caused the greatest problems following the promulgation of the Edict.

The settlement of legal questions was involved. In order to deal with disputes growing out of the Edict or any disputes of a "noncivil nature," special "chambers," or branches, were established in each of the provincial parliaments, or high courts. Equal numbers of Huguenot and Catholic justices would be appointed by the crown to sit on each of these benches.

The Protestants suffered a legal defeat in the capital. A special chamber was added to the Parliament of Paris composed of sixteen justices, ten of them Catholic and six Protestant. This condemned the Huguenots to the position of a permanent minority and ensured their defeat in any case that came before the Paris court. Their only consolation was the knowledge that they would not lose in silence. Their representatives on the bench could and would make their grievances known; and part of a loaf was better than none.

The Edict provided that Huguenot pastors would be paid their wages by the royal treasury, a victory that a number of farsighted Protestants saw as a defeat rather than a victory. Also, these ministers, like their Catholic colleagues, would have no obligations as citizens other than as clergymen. In other words, they could not be drafted into the King's army or navy, they could not be summoned for jury duty, and no other obligations to the state, province or local community could be foisted upon them.

This measure was a source of gratification to the Huguenot clergymen themselves. Now, at last, they had been granted the privileges that Catholic priests had long enjoyed. Therefore, in the eyes of the law they were the equals of the priests.

The military clauses in the Edict were the most complicated, and many pages of the decree were devoted to them. A total of one hundred and three Huguenot towns were granted the right to defend themselves at crown expense. Apparently the details had been worked out by Henry, his Constable and other Protestant generals, and no two towns were granted precisely the same defense rights. Some were allowed to build new castles, town walls, turrets and moats. Others were permitted to strengthen existing defense works. Many were granted combinations of these privileges. Some were given new cannon of various sizes, while others were allowed to build up new arsenals of small arms for the use of individuals.

Virtually every town, depending on its size, was given the right to raise companies, battalions and even large regiments of troops. All of these soldiers were to be recruited from the ranks of Protestant citizens and would be commanded only by Protestant officers. The wages of officers and men would be paid by the royal treasury, and they would be considered crown troops. In the event of a national crisis they, like other troops, would be ordered to make themselves available for duty wherever the crown needed them. At other times, however, they would establish their garrisons in their home towns and would be stationed there for the exclusive purpose of defending those towns.

Although no one, Henry included, seems to have realized it at the time, the effect of the military clauses of the Edict of Nantes was far-reaching. The broad defense privileges granted to the Huguenot towns created something of a state within a state. The Catholic communities had no comparable defense rights, and the Huguenots managed to build up their fortifications so effectively that they were in a position to defy the crown if they chose.

As will be seen in a later chapter, this situation created great difficulties. The Huguenots who had been persecuted for so long felt a natural desire to defend themselves, but neither they nor the Catholics appear to have realized that the building of defense works would cause new tensions between the two segments of the French community.

Other aspects of the Edict of Nantes were considered minor at the time the decree was prepared, but one clause which no one regarded as important had a great impact. Under its terms the Huguenots were permitted to print their own Bible in France and could also publish the writings of Calvin and other "founding fathers" of Protestantism.

No one seems to have been aware of the power of the printed word, but that influence soon made itself manifest after the Edict was promulgated. Scores of printing plants sprang up in the Protestant towns, and soon all of France was flooded with Huguenot Bibles and Protestant tracts.

This, in turn, forced the Catholics to take countermeasures. The hierarchy was anxious to prevent Protestant publications from falling into the hands of faithful Catholics, and feelings on the subject in the Catholic community became bitter. This, as will be seen, contributed to the tragedy that, less than a century after the Edict of Nantes appeared, resulted in its revocation and the renewal of religious persecution.

9

The Edict of Nantes Is Issued

THE Edict of Nantes was in final form no later than mid-December, 1597, and could have been issued at that time. It was not published, however, for more than four months. Protestants in England, Sweden and other countries knew of the decree's existence, and the failure of Henry IV to promulgate it caused considerable criticism of the French monarch. It was claimed that he was tricking the Huguenots and was insincere in his efforts to help them. It was also claimed that he was afraid the decree was too radical and would cause a new religious war in France.

None of the charges against Henry were true. He could have issued the decree the moment it was ready, had he chosen, without fear of new disturbances. His hold on the country was already so great that the Catholics, even though in the majority, would not have dared to rebel against him. On the contrary, as we have already seen, many of the higher-ranking Catholic nobles heartily approved of the principles enunciated in the Edict.

Henry's situation was clear. The Edict was the most revolutionary decree on the fundamental, touchy subject of religion ever written in a civilized land. The mere fact that it would be issued, guaranteeing freedom of conscience to a religious minority, shattered every known precedent.

Catholic laymen approved of some portions and disapproved of others. Protestant laymen approved of some portions and disapproved of others. Even the Catholic cardinals and bishops were in favor of some portions of the document. Only the priests and pastors took the stands expected of them, the former opposing the Edict, the latter approving.

Henry, after consulting with Constable Montmorency, Sully and other advisers, decided it would be wise to gain total acceptance of the Edict *in advance*. In this way he might be able to minimize opposition to it, either in whole or in part, by influential segments of the French population. He also conferred with Cardinal de Bourbon on the idea, and his cousin agreed that his thinking was sound.

The dignity of the King might have been impaired had he taken a direct role in the plan. After all, he could not appear to be asking his subjects to grant him favors. Instead, he decided, his most important subordinates could act in his place. The Duc de Montmorency was chosen to persuade the Protestants that the Edict was good for all, and the Duc de Mayenne was given a similar role to play with the Catholics.

A major responsibility was given to Henry's sister, too. Princess Catherine was a charming, lovely woman who had never taken an active interest in politics. But, like her brother, she felt deeply on religious subjects. She, too, had been reared a

Huguenot and continued to cling to the faith of her childhood. Since her brother's accession to the throne, however, she had formed close friendships with a number of Catholic bishops and was known to be sympathetic to all religions. And so Henry assigned her the task of persuading the cardinals and bishops that the Edict would serve their best interests.

"Catherine," the Duc de Montmorency wrote to his wife, "has begun the formidable enterprise of reconciling the unreconcilable. She will need to exercise her command of the arts of persuasion to the utmost and to use the natural charms with which she is endowed, for surely no woman has ever undertaken a more difficult task. . . . I pray God grant her the ability to soften hard hearts."

All through the early months of 1598 a stream of bishops, abbots and other high-ranking Catholic prelates came to Catherine's palace, the Tuileries. There they dined on what was generally considered the finest food and wine in Paris, and there they listened to Catherine's arguments.

No one knows how effective she may have been, as no records were kept. For whatever their reasons, however, the bishops did not publicly or privately protest the promulgation of the Edict, either individually or in a body. Many of Henry's Huguenot followers had believed they would, and so it is safe to assume that Catherine did some good for the cause of religious freedom and tolerance.

Of all the great men of France, only Biron had no hand whatever in the preparation of the Edict of Nantes or the conferences that followed its completion. At first glance this appears strange, as he held the titles of Marshal, Admiral of

France and Royal Governor of Burgundy. No reason has ever been given for Henry's failure to take his warrior-follower into his confidence.

It may be that Biron, for whatever his reasons, opposed the Edict and therefore was excluded from the deliberations and other proceedings. It is difficult to imagine why he should not have favored the document, since he had risked his life in battle many times for the Huguenot cause.

But Biron was a strange man, and his personal craving for power warped him. He had started life as a poverty-stricken Protestant nobleman of middle rank whose life had been in great jeopardy during the religious wars. Thanks to Henry's generosity he had become a duke. Thanks to Henry as well as his own efforts he was one of two men—Montmorency being the other—who held the exalted title of Marshal of France, the highest rank in the army. His position as Admiral of France was no more courtesy title; he was actually in charge of the vast shipbuilding program. As Governor of Burgundy, a principality that was one of the richest of provinces, he acted as Henry's deputy. In short, he had become one of the most prominent, influential men in France. His standing was easily as great as that of Mayenne, leader of the ancient House of Guise, and in the Royal Council only Montmorency took precedence over him.

But Biron apparently developed the idea that he could take Henry's place. He wanted to rule France himself, and soon after the Edict of Nantes was issued in the spring of 1598 he began to conspire against the crown. He opened secret negotiations with the Grand Duchy of Savoy in the summer of that year, and later he also dealt with Spain. Henry eventually became aware of his activities, and Biron was executed for treason. At the time the Edict of Nantes was published, however, he still stood very high in the King's favor and held all of his great offices.

Active opposition to the Edict developed in two quarters. The rank and file of Catholic priests made no secret of their hatred, and many displayed rare courage by attacking the document from their pulpits. Their opposition was not unexpected, to be sure, and Henry had already taken steps to bring them into line. At his request the bishops directed their subordinates to halt their assaults on the forthcoming decree.

The other source of opposition was a surprise. In virtually every part of France the red-robed justices of the provincial parliaments made it plain that they disliked the Edict and all that it represented. From Normandy in the north to Languedoc in the south the men who administered justice to the King's subjects openly decried the document. Some actually said that they would not obey it.

Henry had two courses of action open to him. If he wished, he could dismiss the judges, imprison or execute them as traitors, and replace them with men more amenable to his wishes. But he knew that drastic action of this sort would reopen the wounds caused by the religious civil wars and would create more problems than it cured. He had no desire to create new martyrs around whom the dissidents could rally.

And so he chose the second course open to him: persuasion. Wanting to keep his efforts unofficial, he decided that his sister should see the justices. The members of the provincial parliaments were invited in small groups to Paris, and there were entertained at the Tuileries.

Sully's *Journal* describes these occasions in some detail. The judges were treated to splendid dinners prepared by Catherine's talented chefs. While they ate the Princess explained the need for tolerance and tried to soothe their fears. The King, she said, had no intention of replacing them. The Huguenot judges who would join the new Catholic magistrates in the special chambers would deal only with religious questions pertaining to the forthcoming Edict.

When a justice remained adamant in his opposition to the Edict, Catherine's manner changed, and her charm vanished. The unfortunate guest suddenly realized that his hostess was a close relative of Henry of Navarre.

Men who refused to work with the King, Catherine calmly explained, might find themselves in personal trouble. Tax collectors would visit them more frequently and would demand every penny due the crown. Sons, brothers and nephews of the stubborn would find it impossible to obtain an appointment to a royal post. And, she confided, her brother was thinking of introducing a new system for the judiciary. Judges no longer would be appointed for life, and present members of the bench would be expected to resign. This, she said, would be purely a courtesy gesture, and most would be reappointed at once, for a few years.

On the other hand, justices who proved loyal to the crown would discover their paths were smoother. Tax collectors would treat them leniently. Their sons and other relatives would be encouraged to apply for crown posts in government. And Henry might even decide to let present judges continue to hold their appointments for life.

The Princess 'tactics were effective, and gradually the justices' opposition to the Edict began to melt away. Only the Parliament of Paris continued to hold out, and a group headed by its President, André Séguier, finally demanded a formal audience with Catherine. The request was granted.

Sully describes the scene. Catherine, in royal purple, was seated on her throne when the deputation arrived, and although she knew all of the justices, she greeted them with a curt nod.

Séguier, as conscious of the armor-clad troops lining the walls of the great hall as he was of the chilly atmosphere, summoned his courage and made an impassioned declaration. He insisted the country would fall into evil hands if the Huguenots were granted places in the parliaments. And he held a threat over the King's head. Under the ancient law of the land, no decree or edict was incorporated into the basic body of French law until it had been ratified by the parliaments.

This, as it happened, was true. An edict became law the moment it was promulgated by the crown, but if vetoed by a parliament, it would theoretically become null and void. Nothing of the sort had happened within the memory of any living man, and it would have been necessary to go back more than one hundred years to find a precedent.

Nevertheless Séguier's hint was very clear. The Parliament of Paris was threatening to veto the Edict.

The situation was so unexpected that Catherine did not know what to do. She remained calm, however, and suggested that the judges adjourn with her to the dining hall for refreshments. They did, and meanwhile she sent a messenger hurrying across Paris to the Louvre. What, she asked her brother, should she do?

According to Sully, he himself was sent to the Tuileries with instructions for the Princess. Catherine directed her servants to give the guests no more food and wine, and she returned with the visitors to the great hall. There she mounted her throne again and made a very brief speech.

"I know full well what is the King's wish in respect to this Edict," she said, "and that he will not do otherwise. He will accept no compromise, and defeat is unknown to him.

"Nor do I myself see any good reason for wishing to prevent those of the Reformed religion, who have been good servants to the King, from entering into the parliaments, seeing that he allowed this right to the Leaguers, who had taken up arms against His Majesty."

The blow struck home. Virtually all of the justices who held places in the Parliament of Paris had been active members of the Catholic League that had fought Henry so bitterly. Their activities alone had delayed his acquisition of the capital. But he had behaved toward them with unusual generosity. Not one member of the Parliament had been dismissed from office; not one had been put on trial for treason.

Catherine's implied threat was as plain as that of Séguier, however. The judges knew she had communicated with Henry, and the Duc de Sully stood at the Princess' side as she made her short address. It was obvious that she was speaking with the full authority of her brother's position.

In brief, Henry could still bring charges of treason against justices who had been members of the Catholic League. If they chose to live in the past, he could forget the new spirit of tolerance he was displaying toward them, too. The royal threat was another Henry IV masterstroke. There might be an outcry if Henry persecuted judges because they opposed a forthcoming edict, but no one in a land where executions were customary would be unduly perturbed if Henry chose to imprison or execute men who had fought him bitterly when he had claimed the crown.

"Madame Catherine," Sully concluded in his *Journal*, "then made other remarks appropriate to the occasion, and the members of the Parliament of Paris withdrew." Unfortunately, no record of these comments has been preserved, but they probably were similar to the other remarks quoted by Sully. In any event, her brief address was effective, and the opposition of the Paris judges to the Edict collapsed overnight. Eventually the Parliament resorted to delaying tactics, as will be seen, but these efforts had no real effect on the Edict.

But the Catholic priests were made of sterner stuff, and they refused to heed the requests of their cardinals and bishops. It may well be that the leaders of the Catholic Church in France were less than vigorous in their demands that their subordinates heed the King's wishes. Since no priest would normally defy the commands of his bishop, who could remove him from his post and order him excommunicated, no other explanation makes sense.

The clause in the Edict that caused the Catholic clergy to rebel was the one pertaining to education. Priests everywhere were outraged by the granting of higher-education rights at

French universities to Huguenots. The priests—and their superiors, it should be noted—regarded the universities and colleges as subsidiary institutions of the Church itself, as much a part of the Church, for example, as Notre Dame. No one bothered to reason that the land, the buildings and the equipment belonged to the crown or that the wages of faculty members and administrators were paid by the royal treasury.

Clerical opposition everywhere in France to the clause was so strong that Henry, much against his will, was forced to take action himself. Late in February, 1598, he summoned the cardinals and archbishops to a meeting at the Louvre and, for the first time since the discussions had begun, lost his temper. He had no intention of backing down, he said. His Edict would provide rights for higher education at French universities to Huguenots. No man would be denied an education on the university level because of his religious beliefs. No matter how hard the priests protested and complained, he did not intend to budge.

That was the end of the matter, he declared, and he directed the cardinals and archbishops to inform their subordinates accordingly.

In the face of the King's open stand, much of the clerical opposition disappeared, but the discontent remained unabated in some sections of the country, particularly in the west. The priests of Nantes remained defiant, as did those of Le Mans, Angers, Rennes, La Rochelle, St. Brieuc and a number of other communities. Six bishoprics were involved, and Henry demanded that the bishops come to Paris. Three sent back word that they were "ill," a fourth begged to be excused for the present on grounds that he was deluged with work, and two others wrote that, much as they wanted to obey the King, they were preparing for a journey to Rome and could not leave their homes for the present.

The delaying tactics of the clergy were effective, but Henry refused to be denied his victory when it was so near. After deliberating the matter in solitude for a day or two, he evolved a new plan as bold as it was forthright. In mid-March he left Paris for the purpose of visiting his loyal subjects in Britanny and other western provinces. Accompanying him were more than two hundred high-ranking nobles of his court and their ladies, as well as three regiments of cavalry, two of infantry and one of artillery. He intended to demonstrate both his majesty and his military power to his stubbornly defiant Catholic clerical subjects in the west.

The party carried silken pavilions and tents for the nobles and ladies; more than two thousand carts were necessary for the food supplies alone; and innumerable servants attended the royal party. There must have been at least three thousand, since no self-respecting member of the nobility went anywhere without an escort of at least a servant or two.

The blue bloods slept in their tents, and only the royalty, like Princess Catherine, became guests at the manor houses of great nobles along the way. Henry himself, wearing armor, lived the simple life of a soldier. He carried only one change of uniform, as he did in time of war, and slept on a small pallet in a simple tent.

The clergymen and nobles of the west did not know whether the King intended literally to wage war on them. Certainly enough soldiers accompanied him to fight a major campaign. Henry, however, said nothing. Occasionally during the weeks of his long, meandering journey, he accepted a dinner invitation at the castle of a duke or some other high-ranking noble. Then, politely, he returned to his simple tent for the night. Often he ate with his troops around their camp fires. Infrequently he joined his party of ladies and gentlemen, who were bored, tired and dirty. Yet his own spirits were high, and he seemed to relish every moment on the road.

At last he reached the towns of the rebellious clergymen. There his attitude remained the same, but he invited the bishops, priests and local nobles to his military camp. There, surrounded by men in armor, with the pavilions of the nobles some distance away, he sat his visitors down for a friendly little chat.

He told them of his hopes for his new Edict. He explained that with it he intended to bring permanent domestic peace to France. And, very blandly, he expressed the hope that no individual or group would try to obstruct the achievement of that goal.

It was one thing for an indignant bishop or priest to defy a monarch in distant Paris. It was another matter entirely for anyone, clergyman or layman, to stand up to Henry IV surrounded by regiments of his veterans, with great lords and ladies supplying window dressing to remind everyone of his royal supremacy.

Bishop after bishop, priest after priest capitulated. None felt any happier about the granting of higher-education rights to

the Huguenots, but there was little that any individual could do when the power of King Henry intimidated him.

Nantes was the last major town on Henry's itinerary, and he reached it on April 10, 1598. On the following day he held his customary chat with the clergymen and nobles of the area, and they, like their colleagues elsewhere, accepted the inevitable.

Henry won his long-range campaign without firing a single shot. He achieved the near miracle of obtaining religious freedom and tolerance for Protestants without the renewal of the dreaded civil wars.

On April 12, 1598, his decree was issued, signed and sealed. It was known as the Edict of Nantes because of circumstance. The King just happened to be in the town of Nantes when he promulgated his Edict.

All that remained at this point was the formal ratification of the Edict by the parliaments. This, however, did not prevent the decree from becoming effective immediately. The "registration," as it was called, was an old custom, and Henry thought it wise to observe tradition. In the days when the parliaments had been powers themselves, a failure to ratify could have created serious trouble for the crown.

But Henry had quietly gathered all the reins of power in his own hands. He wanted the ratification for the sake of posterity. Like so many great monarchs, he was afraid that those who came after him might change, weaken or otherwise warp the great instruments of his reign. Therefore he wanted to make certain that every formality was observed.

Some of the parliaments accepted the inevitable without

fuss. Within a month of its promulgation the Edict was ratified by the judges in the important cities of Lille, Caen and
Lyons. The Parisians saw an opportunity to drag their feet as
a way of showing their disapproval. Séguier and his colleagues
did not dare to incur Henry's open displeasure, but they delayed
interminably.

Henry, having won his victory, could afford to be generous
as well as patient. Month after month passed, and he said
nothing to the Parliament of Paris. By the winter of 1599, however, the citizens of Paris were becoming fascinated by what
they regarded as a dangerous and exciting game. Séguier and
his associates were doing what no one before them had ever
accomplished. They were successfully defying Henry IV.

This unfortunate fact was called to Henry's attention at a
meeting of his Council of State on February 24, 1599. No
man understood the mechanics and technique of rebellion better
than Henry. If he permitted the dissidents of Paris to succeed
in this relatively small matter, others who opposed one aspect
or another of his rule would dare to defy him still more openly.
And eventually a full-scale revolution would break out some-
where in the country.

Not hesitating for a moment, he gave instructions to the
Constable. His directions, recorded by Sully in his *Journal,* were
blunt, as only Henry could be when trouble threatened. "Inform the gentlemen of the Parliament of Paris," he said, "that
I require their signatures no later than tomorrow. If they do
not care to write their names in ink, their blood will suffice."

The Parliament of Paris voted unanimously in favor of the
ratification of the Edict of Nantes, convening at the remarkably

early hour of seven o'clock in the morning for the purpose. No magistrates were absent from the meeting, there was no discussion, and the entire court went at once to the Louvre to make certain the King received the record of their vote before the deadline he had imposed.

The parliaments of about forty other towns continued to delay, but Henry refused to deal with them sternly. It had been necessary for him to crack down on the Parisians, he believed, but if he used similar tactics in forty other places simultaneously, he might well spark the rebellion he had been trying so hard to avoid.

Therefore he used a far more subtle approach. His agents went to the justices of these towns one by one. After the judges of one community had been persuaded to sign, the King's men slowly went on to the next community on their list. Usually they did not approach two towns in the same province within the same half year, preferring to travel far from one end of the realm to the other. In this way they prevented the dissidents in any one province from getting together to air their grievances. It was far easier, too, to deal with the judges in a single town, for they felt that they stood alone against the might of the King.

The last of the courts to ratify the Edict of Nantes was the Parliament of Rouen, which registered the document in March, 1609, almost eleven years after the decree had been promulgated. Meanwhile the Huguenots were reaping the benefits of one of the most remarkable state papers in history.

10

The End of Tolerance, and the New Beginning

By the time Henry IV was assassinated in 1610 by a madman, the people of France had quietly accepted the Edict of Nantes and lived together in peace under its terms. Never had the nation enjoyed an era of such sustained growth and prosperity. A dream of centuries had been realized, and she had become a great power. It is difficult to measure the extent to which this standing could be attributed to the new freedoms accorded the Huguenots, but most historians are inclined to believe that the rights granted to the Protestants played a major role in the expansion of France.

Henry was succeeded on the throne by his son, Louis XIII, and since the new King was only a small child, his mother became Regent until he grew up. Queen Marie was a devout Catholic who turned increasingly for advice, support and help to a remarkable clergyman.

Armand Cardinal de Richelieu was the son of a minor noble who had been a favorite of Henry IV, and he himself had spent his early years at Henry's court. There he became an ardent patriot who learned to share Henry's goals. Gradually moving into posts of greater authority during the regency of Queen Marie, Richelieu became chief minister of France in the early 1620s. He held the position for almost twenty years, continuing to act as the real ruler of the country long after Louis XIII came of age.

Although a high-ranking Roman Catholic prelate, Richelieu was interested in the state, not the Church. Like Henry, he loved power, and, like Henry, he was obsessed by the desire to make France stronger and wealthier. In matters of religious tolerance he was far ahead of his era. An individual's personal faith meant nothing to him, and he gave positions of authority to Huguenots as readily as to Catholics. His one criterion was ability.

Nevertheless a situation arose that brought him into conflict with the French Protestants. During the early years of Marie's regency various high-ranking nobles had begun feuding again, fighting what can best be described as a series of private wars. Some of these lords were Huguenots, and they held a decided advantage over those of their foes who happened to be Catholic. Thanks to the Edict of Nantes, the Huguenot nobles lived in heavily fortified towns and had strong bodies of their own, loyal troops at their disposal.

Richelieu knew these private feuds were harming and weakening the nation, and soon after he became chief minister he took steps to remedy the situation. First he issued a decree prohibiting private warfare. Then, in order to enforce the new law, he ordered the destruction of all castles and all other fortifications in the country not supported by the crown and manned by crown troops.

The Cardinal quickly discovered he had not gone far enough. Under a strict legal interpretation of the Edict of Nantes, the Huguenot forts and castles were crown property, and the soldiers stationed there were crown troops. Rather than create new religious bitterness, however, Richelieu preferred not to take drastic action. Instead he called in the more important Huguenot nobles, one by one, and persuaded them to live at peace with their neighbors.

But in 1627 a major eruption disturbed the peace and could not be ignored. The Duc de Rohan, one of the wealthiest of the Huguenots, decided to create his own kingdom, making the seaport town of La Rochelle on the west coast of France his capital. A number of younger, misguided Huguenot lords flocked to his banner.

The crisis quickly became international. Relations between France and England were very bad at this time, and the English saw an opportunity to embarrass Richelieu. Large sums of money and strong naval and military support were sent to Rohan from London.

At no time was the rebellion serious enough to cause a real civil war. And Richelieu, trying to continue the policies of Henry IV, was striving to make France stronger. Therefore he wanted to avoid an open diplomatic break, much less a war, with England. This left him only one course of action: the suppression of the rebellion.

The task was delicate as well as difficult, and was not accomplished for more than a year. Finally, after great effort and expense, the Duc de Rohan was defeated late in 1628, and his rebellious troops were captured.

Richelieu treated the rebels with wise leniency. No one was executed, no one was deprived of citizenship, and the troops who had taken part in the insurrection were forgiven, although forbidden to bear arms again. Most of the country, including the overwhelming majority of Huguenots, felt horrified and repelled by the rebellion.

But what had happened once could happen again. Men of ambition would be tempted to strike out on their own, either against private enemies or the state itself, when they had their own armies and forts. The suppression of the Rohan rebellion had been costly in money, effort and lives, and the growth of France had been hampered. Richelieu made up his mind that the incident would not be repeated.

"It is sad to relate," he declared, "that in this most civilized of ages there exists, in France, a state within a state. This must not be."

In the Peace of Alais, effected in 1629, the rebellion of Rohan officially came to an end. And in this document Richelieu seized his opportunity to amend the Edict of Nantes.

Under the terms of this treaty, the Huguenots were stripped of their special military privileges. They lost their forts and their private armies. Cannon and small arms, powder and ammunition were no longer supplied to them by the crown. The defense works in some of the one hundred and three Huguenot towns granted the right to build and extend such fortifications were torn down. In others they were rendered inoperable. In those communities where Richelieu's military advisers thought it wise to maintain garrisons in order to protect France from outside enemies, garrisons of troops loyal to the crown were moved in.

The Cardinal took great pains to assure the Huguenot community that he was no bigot and that he was not acting on religious grounds. The need for private Protestant armies and forts, he said, no longer existed. Times had changed for the better, and no man nor community needed to protect itself because of religious reasons.

All other portions of the Edict of Nantes remained intact. The Huguenots continued to enjoy complete liberty of conscience and could worship publicly or privately under the terms of the Edict. They retained full civil and legal rights, and no student was excluded from the universities because of his religion.

Richelieu made certain that the Protestants of France continued to enjoy all of their rights except the military privileges, which he removed. As he explained, no one had cause to protest, inasmuch as the Catholics did not enjoy these privileges, either.

For another half century the Huguenots of France continued to live quietly and peacefully with the Catholic majority.

King Louis XIV, the "Sun King," who ascended the throne in 1643, was as vain as he was brilliant. The process of consolidation of power in the hands of the crown continued unabated during his long reign, which extended into the next century. Eventually the monarchy became absolute. In fact, it was Louis who said, "I am the state."

In his dealings with the Vatican, King Louis maintained and even strengthened the independence that the Catholic monarchs of France had long enjoyed. But it disturbed him when he saw any deviation from what he considered the right path. He envisioned one nation, under the crown, practicing one religion. It would be far easier to control his people, he felt, if all of them were united in all things.

Louis actively resented the presence of people whom he considered heretics among the ranks of his subjects. Religious unity, he become convinced, was essential if France was to become still greater. And it disturbed him that he, the most powerful of all rulers in Europe, was the only one who did not have the right to decide what faith his subjects would practice. Even in England, which was reputed to be liberal, the Anglican Church was the state church, and Catholic worship was forbidden.

Among Louis' advisers were a number of Catholic clergymen who competed for his favor. Knowing how he felt, they suggested that he initiate a policy of trying to convert the Huguenots to Catholicism. The King thought this made good sense, and he enthusiastically agreed.

Relatively few of the Huguenots were willing to accept conversion; the majority resisted, as have all people, everywhere, when attempts have been made to force them to give up their faith. The stubborn attitude of the Protestants infuriated Louis, and he gradually brought more and more pressure, economic and social, to bear against them.

Still they resisted, and in 1683 Louis lost his notoriously short temper. He issued a decree authorizing the stationing of royal troops in the homes of Huguenots for the purpose of *forcing* them to listen to those who were trying to convert them. This bald intimidation merely strengthened the resistance of the Protestants. Fighting back in the courts, they cited the Edict of Nantes, which granted them rights under the law.

When a law did not suit the purposes of Louis XIV, he changed it. The power of the crown had become so great that it was unnecessary for him to consult with anyone before doing what he pleased. Only a few of his closest advisers knew what he had in mind now. In 1685 he suddenly, without advance warning, revoked the Edict of Nantes.

Crown agents quietly went into the slums of Paris and other communities to stir up the people against the Huguenots. The mobs responded as expected, and in the riots that followed, many Huguenots were killed or injured.

Deprived of their precious rights and actively persecuted by the crown, the Huguenots realized that they had no future in France. Large numbers left the country, some going to Holland and the Protestant states of Germany, the majority migrating to British colonies in the New World. There they settled in the frontier districts of Massachusetts and Connecticut, New York and Pennsylvania, where no one was molested because of his faith, and every man was entitled to worship as he pleased.

The Protestants who remained in France either accepted conversion to Catholicism or pretended to accept it. Although no one realized it at the time, many Huguenots continued to practice their own religion secretly. This was not discovered until a century later, when the tearing away of all religious restrictions suddenly revealed the emergence of a fairly substantial group of Huguenots scattered throughout the country.

For slightly more than one hundred years, however, France was officially an exclusively Catholic nation. The practice of no other religion was permitted. Jews as well as Huguenots were persecuted.

Instead of strengthening his nation, Louis XIV seriously weakened it. Most of the French Protestants had been active in commerce, industry and finance. When they disappeared, no one else came along to take their places. French manufacturing, trade and banking went into serious declines. Smaller, less advanced nations became richer and more powerful. Economic decay preceded social and political decay, and the nation gradually became a hollow, rotting shell.

But the Edict of Nantes was not forgotten, even though France slipped from her position as the most enlightened nation in Europe to that of one of the most intolerant. Many Catholics as well as the few remaining Huguenots remembered the happy decades of tolerance and deeply resented the revocation of the Edict of Nantes. Voltaire and other liberal giants of literature kept the spark alive. The universities continued to nourish, subtly, the spirit of the Edict of Nantes.

In 1789 the French Revolution broke out. Economic, political and social conditions had become intolerable for the middle and lower classes. The clergy had grown wealthy, corrupt and indifferent to the welfare of their spiritual charges. The upheaval that followed was one of the most violent in history. King Louis XVI was beheaded, and the monarchy itself was abolished.

Virtually all existing institutions were swept away, among them the Catholic Church. Individuals were allowed to worship God if they wished, but the state proclaimed itself atheist. God, for official purposes, was "banished" from France.

During the many months known as the Reign of Terror, near anarchy gripped France. Thousands of nobles and priests were executed, and thousands of others fled the country. Countless citizens who had done no wrong were denounced by their neighbors who carried grudges against them, and were put to death.

Gradually a more stable, republican form of government was established. And out of the confusion a new leader arose, a worthy successor to Henry IV. Napoleon Bonaparte, the Corsican-born son of middle-class parents, may well be the greatest of all French statesmen-soldiers. The most dynamic general since Alexander the Great and Julius Caesar, he was a many-faceted genius.

Moving up from obscurity, he achieved the position of First Consul, the top position in the government. Not satisfied with this rank, he crowned himself Emperor in 1804 and built a realm that, at one time, covered the better part of Europe.

An avid student of history, Napoleon was thoroughly familiar with the Edict of Nantes and believed in the principles it enunciated. Himself nominally a Roman Catholic, he was passionately convinced that man should have the right to worship God as he pleased or to refrain from worship. He believed that no one should be penalized economically, politically or socially because of his faith or lack of it. On a number of occasions he expressed his admiration for the policies adopted by the new nation across the Atlantic, the United States of America, which granted its citizens complete liberty of conscience.

Late in 1804, a few months after Napoleon had made himself Emperor of France, he told a number of distinguished guests whom he was entertaining at dinner, "No nation can become great unless it abides by the spirit that Henry IV created when he wrote the Edict of Nantes. It is the supreme prerogative of every individual to seek salvation as he elects, or to turn away from it.

"That which Henry IV did must be done again. That which he envisioned must be extended to all. I shall complete the work that Henry IV began."

Napoleon was as good as his word.

France, no longer an atheistic state, permitted men of all faiths to live and work without restriction within her boundaries. Catholics, Protestants and Jews were welcome. All were citizens with equal rights, and all could worship as they pleased.

The expansion of Napoleon's empire brought these same rights to lands that had never before known tolerance. Catholics were allowed liberty of conscience and full civil, legal and personal rights in Protestant countries. The same rights were given to Protestants dwelling in Catholic countries. In many places Jews were set free from the shameful semibondage they had been forced to endure, and the ghettos, or restricted, walled areas in which they had been compelled to live, were abolished.

"All men are equal in the sight of men as well as of God," Napoleon said in a ringing declaration made in 1806.

Goethe, the most renowned of German authors, met Napo-

leon and was overwhelmed by him. Criticized for his adulation by those who claimed Napoleon was a tyrant, Goethe replied, "Does it matter if he comes to us bearing the French flag? Under that flag he grants to all men the most precious of boons, personal freedom. It is the dignity conferred by this freedom that sets men apart from animals. As for me, I will willingly live under any flag that confers such freedom upon all the people."

Napoleon, using the Edict of Nantes as his model, ushered in a new era. In many nations, men who had been persecuted because of their faith now saw religious liberty as a basic right for everyone.

After the defeat of Napoleon by a coalition of his enemies in 1814, an inevitable setback occurred. The forces of repression became active again in many places. Catholics were restricted in some Protestant nations; Protestants, in Catholic nations. In central and eastern Europe Jews were forced back into ghettos.

But the tide of liberation, once set in motion, could not be stilled again. Men who had known liberty could not and would not accept shackles. A series of revolutions rocked Europe in the first half of the nineteenth century. The personal freedoms granted by Napoleon, including freedom of conscience, gradually were restored in one land after another.

Bigotry became aroused in its most virulent form in Nazi Germany between the two World Wars in our own century, but the Nazis were defeated in World War II. Today, in most nations of the earth, the freedom to worship as one wishes, the ideal of Henry IV, has become the accepted norm.

Intolerance, however, has not vanished. The hatreds of centuries persist. Often Catholics, Protestants, Jews, Mohammedans and Buddhists still regard one another with mutual suspicion. Occasionally the rights of a minority group are trampled, subverted or ignored. People are still made to suffer because of their faith.

But mankind is learning and is moving toward the goals set forth in the Edict of Nantes. It is fitting that the ideal of Henry IV, the Huguenot who became a nominal Catholic, should have been given fresh impetus by a Roman Catholic who was one of the giants of the twentieth century. The ecumenical spirit enunciated by Pope John XXIII has fired the imaginations and lifted the spirits of people in every nation. Complete tolerance and brotherly love have not yet been achieved on earth, but man continues to move toward them, and the trend initiated almost four hundred years ago by the Edict of Nantes continues to gain force.

The Edict of Nantes *(Selected Passages)*

Henry, by the grace of God king of France and of Navarre, to all to whom these presents come, greeting:
Among the infinite benefits which it has pleased God to heap upon us, the most signal and precious is his granting us the strength and ability to withstand the fearful disorders and troubles which prevailed on our advent in this kingdom. The realm was so torn by innumerable factions and sects that the most legitimate of all the parties was fewest in numbers. God has given us strength to stand out against this storm; we have finally surmounted the waves and made our port of safety,—peace for our state. For which his be the glory all in all, and ours a free recognition of his grace in making use of our instrumentality in the good work. . . . We implore and await from the Divine Goodness the same protection and favor which he has ever granted to this kingdom from the beginning. . . .

We have, by this perpetual and irrevocable edict, established and proclaimed and do establish and proclaim:

I. First, that the recollection of everything done by one party or the other between March, 1585, and our accession to the crown, and during all the preceding period of troubles, remain obliterated and forgotten, as if no such things had ever happened. . . .

III. We ordain that the Catholic Apostolic and Roman religion shall be restored and reëstablished in all places and localities of this our kingdom and countries subject to our sway, where the exercise of the same has been interrupted, in order that it may be peaceably and freely exercised, without any trouble or hindrance; forbidding very expressly all persons, of whatsoever estate, quality, or condition, from troubling, molesting, or disturbing ecclesiastics in the celebration of divine service, in the enjoyment or collection of tithes, fruits, or revenues of their benefices, and all other rights and dues belonging to them; and that all those who during the troubles have taken possession of churches, houses, goods or revenues, belonging to the said ecclesiastics, shall surrender to them entire possession and peaceable enjoyment of such rights, liberties, and sureties as they had before they were deprived of them. . . .

VI. And in order to leave no occasion for troubles or differences between our subjects, we have permitted, and herewith permit, those of the said religion called Reformed [Protestant] to live and abide in all the cities and places of this our kingdom and countries of our sway, without being annoyed, molested, or compelled to do anything in the matter of religion contrary to their consciences, . . . upon condition that they comport themselves in other respects according to that which is contained in this our present edict.

VII. It is permitted to all lords, gentlemen, and other persons making profession of the said religion called Reform, holding the right of high justice (or a certain feudal tenure), to exercise the said religion in their houses. . . .

IX. We also permit those of the said religion to make and continue the exercise of the same in all villages and places of our dominion where it was established by them and publicly enjoyed several and divers times in the year 1597, up to the end of the month of August, notwithstanding all decrees and judgments to the contrary. . . .

XIII. We very expressly forbid to all those of the said religion its exercise, either in respect to ministry, regulation, discipline, or the public instruction of children, or otherwise, in this our kingdom and lands of our dominion, otherwise than in the places permitted and granted by the present edict.

XIV. It is forbidden as well to perform any function of the said religion in our court or retinue, or in our lands and territories beyond the mountains, or in our city of Paris, or within five leagues of the said city. . . .

XVIII. We also forbid all our subjects, of whatever quality and condition, from carrying off by force or persuasion, against the will of their parents, the children of the said religion, in order to cause them to be baptized or confirmed in the Catholic Apostolic and Roman Church; and the same is forbidden to those of the said religion called Reformed, upon penalty of being punished with special severity. . . .

XXI. Books concerning the said religion called Reformed may not be printed and publicly sold, except in cities and places where the public exercise of the said religion is permitted.

XXII. We ordain that there shall be no difference or distinction made in respect to the said religion, in receiving subjects to be instructed in universities, colleges, and schools; and in receiving the sick and poor into hospitals, retreats, and public charities.

Suggested Reading List

Grundy, Rudolph, *Church and State in the Sixteenth and Seventeenth Centuries*, Philadelphia, 1894.

Howard, Robert L., *France in the Sixteenth Century*, New York, 1913.

——, *Henry the Great, King of France*, New York, 1910.

Lewis, Paul, *Lady of France*, New York, 1963.

Lindsay, T. M., *History of the Reformation*, London, 1907.

MacGregor, M. K., *The Protestant Champion, Henry of France*, 2 vols., Philadelphia, 1938.

Street Ballads of the Sixteenth and Seventeenth Centuries, ed. by Jacques Sorel, Paris, 1838; translated by R. O. Fisher, London, 1859.

Tilley, A. A., *Cambridge Modern History*, Vol. II, Cambridge, 1902.

Thompson, Ronald Edwin, *Free to Worship God*, Boston, 1947.

A Note About the Author

NOEL B. GERSON is the author of some two dozen historical and biographical works, including *Give Me Liberty*, *The Swamp Fox*, *I'll Storm Hell*, *Sam Houston* and a popular modern novel, *Jefferson Square*. A former newspaper foreign correspondent and World War II Military Intelligence officer, Mr. Gerson has lived in many parts of the world. He holds B.A. and M.A. degrees in American history from the University of Chicago.